for

Sîan

CaymanStar

with best wishes

Elizabeth Brown

Elizabeth Brown

The love expressed in
This Story is True

Fleet Publishing

First published in The United Kingdom in 2011 by Fleet Publishing Ltd

www.fleetpublishing.com
email: info@fleetpublishing.com
Fleet Publishing Ltd. PO Box 6748, Wolverhampton WV6 6FF

ISBN: 978-0-9570014-1-1

A CIP catalogue record for this title is available from the British Library.

Typeset by Troubador Publishing, Leicester
Printed and bound by CPI, Croydon

Photographic editing (except 'As summer came we did more jumping.')
and cover design by Depinder Juttla

Photographs reproduced with kind permission of copyright owners:
'Falconwood' – My father. © Sharon Houghton
'We'll see if we can sell him in 'Horse and Hound'". © Alison Goodwin.
'As summer came we did more jumping.' © Eqipics
Cayman, Harrison, Toby, Lucy. © Graham Jones.

All other photographs courtesy of the author.

CaymanStar

The True Story of a Horse's Life

Dedicated to

Cayman

and all horses,
for their wisdom, beauty, spirit and dignity
and for the magical spell that they cast over the lives
of those whom they choose to have the honour of caring for
them.

CONTENTS

ILLUSTRATIONS

ACKNOWLEDGEMENTS

My sincere thanks to these special people:

Pat and Ted Brown, my parents, for unstinting love and support for me and Cayman.

Samantha Fish and Liz Fiddler, for a heroic dash with Cayman to Liverpool. Tina Smith and Laura Denning, for knowledgeable assistance when it was urgently required. Edward Evans and Laura-Jayne Bown, Cayman's friends in a time of need. Sue Taylor, Cayman's vet, for making his journey to Liverpool more bearable. Prof. Barry Edwards, Dr. Dylan Gorvy and Eva O'Donoghue of Liverpool University Veterinary Hospital, for their immense skill and compassion.

Judith Heywood, my best friend, for 'picking up the pieces'.

Will Fish, for years of sound equestrian advice. Everyone at Gunstone Hall, for their kindness.

The late Julie Dicker, who carefully helped Cayman.

Gillian Mackay, Alison Goodwin, Lisa Smith, Sarah Dakin and Jennifer Blenkiron, for their empathy.

Kia and Kris Balle Kristensen for enlightenment and hope.

Sharon Moules Houghton (née Moules Jones),
for introducing me to Falconwood.

Ricky (the reluctant horseman).

Bal de Vini, for help with typing, and Laraine Beranic for dedicated reading.

Chapter One

WHEN I WAS YOUNG

*M*y mother was called Dora, she was grey like me. When I was a little foal I thought that she was so tall that she went all the way to the top of the sky. She had strong legs with silky white hair at the back of her hooves and a round rump. Her grandfather was a Shire horse, she told me that he was magnificent, standing up huge and strong. He could work all day long, his enormous hooves pounding the earth with each powerful step. His name was Hercules. The rest of my mother's family were Irish Draught horses, they were also tall with strong legs and powerful hindquarters.

My father Falconwood was the kindest stallion on earth, he was a dark bay Thoroughbred. His family were racehorses and showjumpers who could gallop fast and jump well.

My mother was with me all the time, she was kind and her smell comforted me. When I was very young she guided me by gently pushing me with her nose. As I got a bit older and started to explore our field, she kept a watchful eye on me all the time. When I was suddenly scared by something I did not expect, I would run back to hide under her belly as fast as I could, I was always safe and warm there. There were other foals and their mothers in our field, but only *my* mother let me hide under her belly. Once, when I got muddled up and tried to hide under the wrong mother I very nearly got kicked.

I had a shock the first time I would not fit under my mother's belly. I panicked. I did not know where to go to hide. I realised that this must mean that I was growing. Bits of me seemed to be growing more than others. My feet were always big and my legs were long, but then my head and ears grew and the rest of me did not, so I felt funny. I was nearly black, but my tail was white. I wondered whether I had the right tail. It was confusing to be me.

I was cheeky and naughty sometimes. I liked to play at springing, bucking, and running with my tail in the air as fast as I could, so that my mother could not catch me; but she was always patient and kind.

We lived in an old field with banks to play on and hedges with rabbit holes underneath. It was on a farm called "Bodernog" in the north of Anglesey. I thought that we would live there forever, but then one day, when I was only about six months old, my mother told me that she would be having another foal so she had to go and live in a field on the other side of the farm. Now that I was getting big she said that I could stay in the field without her; the other foals would keep me company. I was very frightened. I did not want my mother to go, it was the worst thing I could think of.

Soon the farmer came to our field with his daughter, put head collars on my mother and my friend Gwyn's mother, and led them both out of the field. Gwyn and I were eager to trot along by our mothers' sides, even though the sharp ground pricked our feet.

We reached the farmyard and followed our mothers into a big shed. What happened next was the most frightening thing that had ever happened to me. The farmer was between me and Gwyn and our mothers, who were very quickly led out of the shed by the farmer's daughter; this time, we could not follow them. No sooner was my mother's rump out of the doorway than both the bottom and top doors were slammed shut. Gwyn and I were trapped.

We ran round the shed, bumping into each other and neighing as loudly as we could for our mothers to come back. We could hear our mothers neighing to us from outside, they sounded very worried. Gwyn and I neighed so much that our neighs seemed to be the only sound in the world. We neighed for a long time. When we stopped neighing it was suddenly very quiet. I was exhausted and the loneliest I had ever been in my life. It got dark, the night seemed to go on forever. We were very frightened without our mothers. There was water and hay in the shed, but neither of us felt like eating it. We did not sleep at all.

Early in the morning, we heard footsteps and then the top

door opened. Although it was still dark we could see the farmer. We hoped that he had come to take us back to our mothers, but he just threw some more hay into the shed for us and quickly closed the top door again. We were hungry by now, so we did eat some hay, but it did not make us feel better. We were glad that we had each other for comfort. It was strange to be shut in the shed and we missed our mothers very much.

The farmer or his daughter continued to give us more hay and water. They came into the shed to check that Gwyn and I were alright and had not injured ourselves. When the door opened we could feel the cold air from outside; it was warm in the shed. We stayed in the shed for a long time. Eventually the farmer left the top door open during the day so that we could see out into the yard.

The vet came; he stuck sharp things into our necks which made us go to sleep. When I woke up I could not see properly, or get up, it was frightening. Between my back legs ached, it really hurt. Gwyn said that he felt the same. We both smelled strange and all we wanted to do was sleep. Very slowly, the pain and the strange smell went away, until after a few days we were back to normal.

It started to get a bit warmer and brighter outside. We seemed to have been inside for so long that when the farmer and his daughter came to let us out of the shed, it felt odd to be outside again. We were put back in our old field, but this time there was just me and Gwyn and the other foals, their mothers must have gone to the other side of the farm to have foals too. We remembered our mothers, but we were no longer worried or frightened to be by ourselves. We were happy together and we could play whatever games we wanted, whenever we wanted.

I grew and grew. I wondered whether I was going to become as magnificent as my great-grandfather Hercules, it certainly seemed possible.

In the summer when I was two, the farmer came to our field and put a head collar on me. Gwyn and the other youngsters put their heads up to look at what the farmer was doing, but when they could see that he was only handling me, they soon got back to grazing. There was so much lovely grass that they hardly noticed the farmer leading me round the edge of the field. I had to walk alongside the farmer and concentrate hard on where to put my feet, I did not want to tread on him. I thought that being led was strange. I already knew where to go. I did not see the point of it, but if it was what the farmer wanted to do, I did not mind. Perhaps he was lonely. Anyway, I liked the smell of his big old coat, and after he took the head collar off, he rubbed my forehead and quietly gave me a handful of feed from his pocket. Gwyn and the others did not notice.

The farmer could tell that I was not going to be troublesome, so the next time he led me out of the gate and onto the lane that went to the farmyard. The lane felt stony to my feet, but if I stayed on the grass in the middle, it was easier to walk.

I got used to being led and it was interesting to see more of the farm. I liked the cats that lived in the yard. They did not come hunting up to my field; they said that there were more than enough rats and mice for them to chase in the buildings around the yard, so they were far too busy to bother with my field. I knew that they were just boasting though, because whenever there was a patch of sunshine in the yard, there was always a cat asleep in it.

The three collie dogs who lived in the yard were always with the farmer when he came up the lane to check the sheep. They barked a lot, but the sheep were not really scared of them and neither was I.

Later, in the spring before I was three, the farmer put a saddle on my back for our walks, I did not mind that. It felt strange to start with because it was fastened onto me by a thick band behind my front legs that went right round my chest. I thought that it might stop me from breathing. I was a bit scared, but I soon forgot about it when I had no trouble breathing.

Next, there was a bridle – that was more of a problem because when the farmer first tried to put it over my ears, he couldn't – they would not fit. He made it longer at the sides, then it fitted. I did not really like the bit though. It was in my mouth but I could not chew it, let alone swallow it. It just stayed there annoying me, but I could not spit it out because it was attached to the straps that went up my cheeks. I could not see the point of it at all.

The farmer must have known that I was not happy; the next time he put the bridle on me there was some very sticky stuff on the bit. It nearly stuck to my lips before it was even in my mouth, but when it was in my mouth, I tasted the sweetest taste that I had ever tasted in my life. I did not notice the bit any more, my mouth was so full of the lovely sweetness.

Now I had to do a different sort of leading, it was on a long lead. To start with, I was so confused that I stood still, trying to work out what to do. The farmer told me to "Walk on !" and made a long stick with a thin snake on the end touch my back leg, that frightened me and made me go forwards, but he kept tight hold of the long lead so that instead of going somewhere, I went round in a circle. That seemed to be what he wanted because he made me do it a few times, first one way and then the other, sometimes walking, sometimes trotting. To start with I could not get my balance, which made me buck, but once I got used to this sort of leading, it was quite easy. I was glad that I did not have to do it for too long though because it was not very interesting.

My mother had told me that when I grew up I would be 'a riding horse' which meant that I would carry a person on my back. She said that this was not as difficult as it sounded and that if you had the right person, it could be fun. So, I was not surprised when the farmer's daughter got onto my back. The farmer and his daughter did seem surprised when I just stood there. When the farmer's daughter squeezed my sides gently with her legs and said: "Walk on!" I did what she asked and when she made the bit press the corners of my mouth and said: "Whooa", I worked out that she must want me to stop going forwards, so I halted. I had to walk and then halt a few times before the farmer's daughter stroked my neck, told me that I had been good and got off my back. Being ridden was much easier than I had expected.

Each time the farmer's daughter rode me for longer; she made me trot with her still on my back. That felt funny, I was worried that it would make her fall off, but it did not. I thought that she was very clever to balance on my back.

I was quite content with things as they were, so I got a big surprise when the farmer said to his daughter:

"Now he's been backed it's time he went, can't have him doing nothing forever."

I was offended; I did not do nothing! I played games in the field with my friends, I talked to the rabbits who lived under the hedge and the sheep in the next field, the farmer's daughter rode me, I ate grass and snoozed. What more was there to do? Anyway, where would I go? I did not know anywhere else. I was worried by what I had heard. I felt very unsettled.

'Falconwood' – My father

Chapter Two

MY NEW HOME

People

had not seen many people in my life; there was the farmer, and his wife who would stroke my neck gently and talk soothingly to me when I went for walks through the farmyard with the farmer. There was the farmer's daughter who rode me, the vet, and the man who drove the milk tanker. Those were all the people I had ever seen. I liked people, I was interested in the clever way they walked on two legs. I thought that it was strange that they seemed to have manes but no tails. I liked the sound of their voices which went up and down a lot, and I tried hard to understand what they were saying – but that was difficult.

It was a lovely surprise when two new people came into my field with the farmer one evening. One was a lady – she had a long bright mane, the same colour as a fox. The other was a tall thin man. I walked up to the people and stretched out my neck to smell them. They were friendly; the lady put out her hand and slowly walked towards me. I let her stroke my cheek. As she did so, I stretched my neck as far as I could and smelled her mane, it smelled comforting. I let her stroke my neck, which gave me a chance to nuzzle her pockets to see whether they had any feed in them like the farmer's pockets – they did not. The farmer put on my head collar, and the tall thin man walked round me, looking hard at my legs and feet. He then walked round me again, this time looking at my body, stopping directly behind me and directly in front of me. No one had ever looked at me so hard, I felt a bit nervous and kept one ear pointed to him all the time. With my other ear I listened to the farmer and the fox mane lady. They were talking quickly so it was impossible for me to understand. They said something about "England", but I did not know what that was. As I was on a long rope, I decided to eat some grass whilst they talked around me. After a while the farmer rubbed my forehead and took off my head collar. The people followed the farmer out of my field and I soon forgot about them.

A Long Journey

I was standing in my field thinking about whether I should sit down for a while and nibble the grass that I could reach around myself, or whether I should look for mayweed on the dry patch by the gate, when a lorry pulled up in the gateway. I was surprised when the farmer jumped out of one side of the cab and another man, whom I had never seen before, jumped out of the other side. The farmer had my head collar in his hand. As he opened the gate, he said to the other man:

"I don't think he'll be any trouble, he's quiet enough."

I sensed that something was going to happen. I stood up tall and put my head up to get a better look at the lorry. It was not shiny like the milk tanker – it looked quite battered and old. The farmer put on my head collar:

"Come on boy, time to go."

I knew that the lorry had something to do with me going. I hoped that the other man knew *where* to go, because I certainly didn't. I felt confused, but interested in what would happen next. The farmer led me out of the gateway as the other man put the ramp at the back of the lorry down. I could see that there was already a brown horse in the lorry. He was smaller than me. I liked him, he had mud on his rump and in his tail, just like me. He was busy pulling hay from the big net in front of him. There was a partition and an empty space at the side of him, with another big hay net. Even though the ramp wobbled when I put my foot on it, and I had to put my head down to fit in the lorry, I could smell the hay and could not wait to get to it. The farmer seemed surprised that I was in the lorry so quickly. As the ramp went up he said:

"O.K. Malcolm, let's see what we can get for him over there." I heard the lorry start up, it was difficult to keep my balance as it moved, but I was not scared. I had all the hay I could eat, and a new friend – he said that his name was Dewi.

The air changed, I could smell a fresh, salty smell. Dewi told me that we were going over a sea made of water, which was like a stream, but bigger. I did not know what a stream was, let alone a sea. I knew what water was though, it was in the trough in my field and it was made of rain. I was not really bothered, I felt safe in the lorry with Dewi. I ate so much hay that I felt very content and the noise of the lorry made me feel a bit sleepy, although I could not sleep properly because sometimes the lorry moved suddenly and jolted us.

After a long time, the lorry seemed to be going over some very bumpy ground and then it stopped. We could hear men's voices, one was Malcolm's, and then the ramp was let down. Malcolm came into the lorry and checked us both, he untied Dewi and let him walk slowly backwards out of the lorry and down the ramp. He came back, untied me and backed me down the ramp, it was good to be able to stretch my legs and to be in the fresh air. Malcolm held my rope whilst I ate some grass, as he talked to the other man, who was holding Dewi's rope. Malcolm then led me round in circles, I did not see the point of this, I wanted to eat more grass. Eventually Malcolm led me to the lorry again, I was eager to get back to the hay, so I walked up the ramp, put my head down and went in. Dewi stayed outside with the other man.

Gunstone Hall

The lorry set off again, this time I had no one to talk to, but there was plenty to eat, so I was alright. The next time the lorry stopped I heard a lot of dogs barking, they sounded close by. I could tell that two of them were collies, like on my farm. When the ramp went down, another man came into the lorry and untied me. He was sturdy and gentle, he backed me carefully down the ramp, his voice was comforting and I felt safe.

The dogs were all still barking, there were a lot of them, little ones and bigger ones. I was not afraid of dogs, I was already used to them. The man led me towards some buildings:

"Come along Malcolm, let's find you a stable." I was surprised, *I was not Malcolm!* he was the man who had driven the lorry. This new man who was looking after me was very kind, but I really did *not* want him to call me Malcolm.

In the stable there was some hay on the floor, but it was different. It made my muzzle sticky and tasted sweet, it was much better than any hay I had ever eaten. I decided that if this man was going to feed me on hay like this, he could call me whatever he wanted, *even* Malcolm.

Wash and Brush Up

I woke up early the next morning, I was confused. I had been dreaming that I was in my field at home on Anglesey, playing with the rabbits at dawn, but when I opened my eyes there was a white wall in front of me. I did not know what had happened, but slowly I remembered my journey with Dewi. I stood up and tried to look outside, but opposite the entrance to my stable there was a path and another wall, so I could not see out. I neighed to see whether anyone else was awake. That made all the dogs start barking madly. I was not sure what to do next, but then I noticed some bits of the lovely hay that I had missed the night before and decided to concentrate on searching my stable thoroughly for food.

I occupied myself for a long time like this, then I heard people's voices approaching my stable, and footsteps. As they got nearer, I heard a voice that I recognised, but I was still very surprised when the fox mane lady from Anglesey came into my stable:

"Hello lad, didn't expect to see me here did you?" I certainly did not. I wondered whether the tall thin man would appear, and perhaps even the farmer. I heard more footsteps, heavier than before and looked over the rail at the entrance to my stable. The gentle sturdy man was coming down the path:

"Hello Malcolm!" I was starting to get used to that name. As the fox mane lady ducked under the rail, he said:

"Hi Alison, are you ready to give this one a wash and brush up?"

I was led out onto the yard where all of the dogs barked at me again. One of the collies, who was the leader, told me that they knew that I was not frightened, but as their job was to guard the yard, barking was what their people expected them to do, so they did it to keep them happy. That way, he said, there was no risk of their people stopping feeding them. I understood and did not mind them barking at me at all. To make it look as if they were doing their job really well, I made my eyes wide, held my head up high and even snorted a bit.

We walked to a wall by a trailer with a muck heap in it. Alison asked the man:

"Are you going to wash him Will?"

I was learning fast, the gentle sturdy man's name was Will. I was not at all prepared for what happened next though. Will tied me up close to what looked like a sleeping snake, connected to a metal thing. I looked at the snake hard, but as it really did seem to be asleep, I was not worried by it. Will moved the metal thing and the snake seemed to be waking up, it twitched and jumped and made a hissing sound. I was alarmed. Will got hold of the snake, pointed its head at the ground and rain came out of it. Will was talking to me in a quiet voice; he looked strong and could obviously conquer a snake. I knew that Will was the snake's master because when he twisted its head, the rain stopped and when he twisted it again, it started. The snake did exactly what Will wanted it to do.

Whilst Alison stood by my head and stroked my neck, Will pointed the snake at my shoulder and made the rain fall on me softly, I did not mind. Next, Will made the rain fall on my back, then on my rump. Will scrubbed my rump with a brush, which reminded me of scratching my rump on the low branch of the old dead tree in my field at home. It felt very good to have my rump scratched.

Alison put some cold stuff on my mane and rubbed all along it. Will put it on my tail, its smell was like flowers. Will rubbed the top of my tail. I was enjoying having so much attention. Will made the rain fall on my mane. I thought that it might go in my ears, or worse still, in my eyes, but it did not. As the rain fell on my mane, shiny white lumps – like snow – fell off it onto the ground. I was surprised, I had not known that there were shiny white lumps on my mane. As they sat on the ground and more rain fell on them, they vanished. When Will made rain fall on my tail I could just see, out of the corner of my eye, that the same thing happened there. The shiny white lumps which lived on my mane and tail were strange, but I did not worry about them, I felt safe with Will and Alison.

Alison scraped the rain off my neck and my body, put a rug on me and led me back into my stable. Some more hay had been put on the floor for me to eat, I was happy here. When I was dry, Alison came into my stable and tied me up. This time she stood close to my neck, on a crate that made her as tall as me. She combed my mane carefully and then started pulling it out. This did not hurt, but I could feel her quickly tugging at small parts of it, just a few hairs at a time. I wondered why she had taken the trouble to wash my mane if she wanted to pull it out? Having Alison standing close to me was comforting. I had eaten a lot of hay and felt sleepy, so I closed my eyes and had a snooze. I must have snoozed for quite a long time because when I woke up, Alison was no longer by my neck. She was behind me, bending down, studying my tail before holding the bottom and cutting some off.

I was afraid that if my mane was pulled out and my tail cut off, I would have nothing to protect me from flies, cold and rain. Alison stood up straight:

"There you are – all done!"

I was relieved. I certainly felt different, my mane was still there, but it felt light and moved more when I shook my neck. My tail also felt lighter, it was easier to swish, and there was the smell of flowers all around me.

"Horse and Hound"

I felt like a different horse when I woke up the next morning; I was so clean and I still smelled of flowers. I did not feel like me. I was excited. I wondered what new things I would be doing that day. It was not long before Will came towards my stable, carrying a saddle and bridle:

"Hello Malcolm, let's see if these fit you."

After rubbing my forehead, Will put the bridle against the side of my face, then he undid some of the straps so that he could move the buckles, before doing them up again. When Will put the bridle on me, it was comfortable.

I knew that Will was someone whom I could trust, so I did not even mind when he did up a strap under my chin that I was not used to, which made it impossible for me to open my mouth. Next, Will put the saddle on my back and steadily tightened the girth. I could also feel a new strap down the middle of my chest, but I was not bothered about that either. As he led me out of the stable into the sunshine, I thought that we might be going for a ride in this new place, but he said:

"Right, let's get you into the garden."

I knew what a garden was, there was one at my farm on

Anglesey, but the farmer there said that I must not go into it, because my hooves would make holes in the lawn and I might eat the flowers. I could not believe my luck, Will actually wanted me to go into the garden! I had forgotten that there was a strap under my chin that stopped me from opening my mouth. All I could think of was grazing on the lawn, and maybe eating some flowers.

Will led me across the yard to a tall wooden door in a wall. He opened the door and I saw the loveliest garden in front of me. There was a lawn as big as a field, flowers, and in the distance a beautiful lake.

Alison came out of the house with another lady. As they approached me, I could tell that they were impressed by my appearance. I thought that they were going to stroke me and praise me a lot and then let me eat the lawn. Instead, Alison was concentrating on a square metal thing that she was holding and the other lady put a wooden crate just behind my left front leg. She held my reins whilst Will put a hard shiny hat on his head. Will stood on the crate and then leaned over the saddle. He stayed in that position for a while, with his legs on one side of me and his arms and head on the other side. He talked quietly to me and stroked my shoulder. Then, very gently, Will put one leg over my back, so that he was sitting in the saddle, but he was still crouched near to my neck and carried on stroking my shoulder and talking to me. Gradually, I felt him straighten up and put his feet in the stirrups:

"Seems O.K. Sam, just let him go a bit."

As the lady who was holding my reins stepped away from

me, Will squeezed my sides with his legs and I walked forwards across the soft, springy lawn. I was not at all bothered about having Will on my back, he made me feel safe. I looked around at my surroundings. Although everything was new, it did not feel strange. I was glad that I had come to this place, it looked as if it would be a good place to live.

When we got near to the fence which separated the garden from the field with the lake in it, we halted. Alison came down the lawn towards us, still with the square metal thing in her hand. She stopped and held it up to her eyes – it made a sudden sound that surprised me.

"Where are you going to advertise him?" she asked Will.

He replied: "We'll see if we can sell him in 'Horse and Hound' first, if we can get a good enough picture."

I did not really understand what Alison and Will had said, but I did know the word "sell". My mother had told me that it is a word that horses usually dread, because it means that you will be sent away. I was frightened. I thought that I had just been sold, and that was why I was here. I did not want to be sold again. Why couldn't I live in this garden for ever? Why didn't Alison, and Will, and Sam, want me any more? I was confused – and worried.

"We'll see if we can sell him in 'Horse and Hound'"

Chapter Three

FINDING A PERSON

Part One

I was not allowed to stay in the garden. I was put out in a big field with the other geldings, there were about twenty of us. The other geldings were all shapes, sizes, colours and ages. I had never seen so many horses all together before. It was exciting to be amongst them and most of them were friendly towards me. I was the youngest, but because of my size, I did not get bullied. The younger horses were playful and the very old ones did not want to be bothered at all. I quickly settled down and learned who was who, but although I was only three, playing with the other youngsters was not the most important thing. I remembered that my mother had said that when I grew up, I would be a riding horse and that if you had the right person this could be fun. I did not want to be sold. I did not want to leave this place, so I knew what I must do; I had to find a person.

It was fortunate that there did seem to be a lot of people to choose from. On one side of my field was a lane with people coming and going all day. But, even better, there was a foot path right along the side of my field nearest to the lake. People came over the bridge across the stream into the field and walked along the edge, where I could get up close to them, before they climbed over the stile onto the lane.

So, I set about finding a person. I spent hours grazing by the fence along the lane. Sometimes people walking on the lane would stop and try to stroke me. That was difficult because the lane was lower than the field, there was a ditch, a bank, a wooden fence and then a tape fence, between them and me, and as I was already nearly 17hh and they were lower down, all they could do was reach my nose. Most just told me how enormous I was, others laughed at my big feet, some seemed frightened of me, which made me sad.

I tried to stand in the gateway, which was lower, as much as I could, but that was a problem because there were often horses and their people going in and out. I was sad that all of the horses in my field had at least one person, some had more than one, but I did not even have one person of my own.

When people came walking along the footpath I would walk behind them. Often they would look over their shoulder and walk faster, so I would walk faster. If the people had a dog with them, the dog would also look over its shoulder at me, put its tail between its legs and try to get in front of its person.

I was not having much luck finding a person of my own. Then, one morning in autumn, when the sun made everything golden, I was standing on the high ground, near to the foot path, snoozing in a sun ray, when two ladies walked up the footpath from the stream, towards me. As they got nearer, I felt one of them looking at me, she did not take her eyes off me. Usually it made me feel nervous when people looked at me so much, but this person was different. She walked steadily, straight towards me, stopping a short distance away. As if a spell had been cast over her, she stood and gazed at me. I had never seen a person behave like this before. I drew myself up to my full height, but I did not want to move away from her.

Slowly, the lady stretched out her hand – and gently came closer, so that she could stroke my neck. She stroked my neck with more kindness than I had ever felt from a person before.

She stepped back. I did not move at all as she walked round me slowly and calmly, gazing at me – and talking to me in a quiet and reassuring voice. She stood by my head:

"You don't look very old – let me look at your teeth." She slipped her hand round my nose and gently lifted my top lip up and my bottom lip down. I liked her standing close to me, I felt safe.

"So many baby teeth! I think you're only three." As the lady stroked my cheek and looked into my eye, it felt as if a spell was on both of us and I knew that, at last, I had found my person.

"Come on Liz, we need to get going!" The other lady was standing close to the fence. It was like being woken up. For a while Liz stayed by me, I could tell that she did not want to go.

As soon as Liz did move away from me, I felt the gap between us and as she walked to the fence, the gap got bigger and bigger. I did not like the feeling, so I quickly walked after her. I had nearly caught up with her when Liz climbed over the stile onto the lane. I stood by the stile with my head up high so that I could see Liz. I did not want her to go. I wanted her to come back. I wanted her to stay and be my person. How could I get her back? I did not know what to do. I waited by the stile, but Liz did not come back. I neighed. I was confused. I knew that when she had stood by me and looked into my eye, Liz was under the same spell as me, she could not just go. I wanted her to be next to me again. I felt the gap for days, it made me sad.

Being Vetted

Will came into my field with a head collar:

"Come on Malcolm, we've got to get you vetted." He led me up the lane and into the yard. This time, instead of taking me into the garden, he led me into a very big building with bright lights, the ground felt soft under my feet.

Sam was there, and Alison. There was another lady, she looked at me and said to Will:

"He's a big chap – looks useful." Will put a different head collar on me, this one had a very thick band round my nose, with metal rings on it, it fitted tightly. He clipped a long rope onto the middle ring on the nose band. The new lady approached me and I was alarmed to see that she had a snake on her! It came out of both of her ears and its head, which dangled down her chest, seemed to be moving. My eyes widened, my nostrils flared, my ears pointed as far forward as they would go. I could not understand why the lady did not seem to be at all concerned about having a snake on her. I was frightened of it and it was not even on me.

I knew that Will could conquer a snake, but this one was much more dangerous than the one by the trailer, it had somehow wrapped itself round the lady's head and was coming out of her ears. Will stroked my neck:

"What's the matter lad? – It's alright." The lady stroked my shoulder and also tried to reassure me as she pressed the snake's head behind my front leg. I was in between two people who had no idea how dangerous a snake can be and now the snake was on me and they were telling me that I need not worry!

I was trying to work out what to do next when the lady took the snake's head off me and said to Will:

"O.K. you can lunge him for ten minutes in trot." I was glad to have been released from the snake; it must have been in a good mood as it did not bite me. I hoped that it would not bite the lady.

I knew what trotting on the lunge was, I had done it at home on Anglesey, it was not difficult. As I trotted round and round, I heard the door open and someone came in, but I could not see who it was because Will kept me trotting round quickly. I was getting tired, I seemed to have been trotting round in circles for ever. If I slowed down, Will urged me on by making a clicking noise. I got so used to trotting round in circles that I thought that even if I wanted to stop, I would not be able to, my feet just seemed to keep going by themselves.

Eventually Will did call out:

"Woaaaaahhh! – Malcolm –Waaaaaalk." Without me telling them what to do, my feet slowed to a walk. I walked round for a couple of circles, then when Will said:

"Malcolm – Haaaaalt!" I stopped. I was out of breath and my sides were heaving.

As I watched the lady with the snake in her ears walk towards me, I saw that there were now two people sitting in the corner, one was Alison and although I could hardly believe my eyes, the other person looked like Liz. I scarcely noticed the snake lady put the snake's head on my chest again.

Before I could do anything, Will made a clicking noise for me to walk on, and then another, for me to trot on briskly. Again, I was going round in circles.

I tried desperately to look into the corner to see if Liz really was there, but I was going too fast and it was confusing even to try to work out where the corners were.

That trot seemed to go on forever. All I wanted to do was get a good look at the other person in the corner. After what seemed like all the time in the world, Will slowed me down and halted me again. Thank goodness! I was facing the corner where Alison was and the person who had been with her was walking towards me; I could see that this was Liz. I was so glad that I forgot how tired and out of breath I was.

Liz held out her hand as she got closer: "Hello Lad."

I was glad to hear Liz's voice again. She stroked my neck with the same kindness as the first time in the field; I felt more happiness than I had ever felt before. Liz had come back! Maybe she wanted to be my person. I really wanted her to be.

Will led me round the building a few times, to let me get my breath back and cool down, before leading me out into the yard, past the trailer with the sleeping snake, and into some more stables. We kept on going until we got to the stables at the back, where Will led me into the corner stable; it was quite dark. The snake lady came into the stable, but the snake was no longer on her, I wondered where it had gone. Perhaps it was still in the big building with bright lights. It is always better to know where dangerous things are.

"This is the best one Sue – it's pretty dark," Will said. Now I knew the snake lady's name too. When she shone a very bright light into my eyes, one at a time and looked closely at them, it made each eye go blind for a while; I hoped that Sue knew what she was doing. I was pleased that my eyes still worked, because as each eye recovered, I could still see Liz. She was now standing outside the stable; she looked as if she understood that it was all a bit strange for me.

I was led back into the yard again and Sue held up one of my front legs so that the underneath of my hoof was touching my elbow. She held it like that for so long that it felt as if it would never straighten again. Suddenly, and all at once, Sue put my foot down as Will made a loud clicking sound and pulled me into a fast trot up the yard. As Will led me, still at a trot, down the yard, I could see that Liz was standing near to Sue, watching me trot. Liz seemed to be concentrating very hard on how I trotted. So, when Will asked me to trot up and down the yard again, after Sue had held up my other front leg, I made sure that I did my very best trotting. I think that Liz was impressed, she was looking at me kindly, like she had done in the field and she was smiling.

Next, Will led me to a stable nearer the garden, which was brightly lit by sunlight. Will went off and I had to stand still whilst Sue looked carefully all over me for whorls in my hair. She seemed to be writing down where they were, which was mostly on my neck and on my chest. Liz was still watching quietly from outside the stable. I started to doze off, but I woke up with a start when Sue called out to Liz: "Will he be your first horse?"

I was so surprised to hear what Sue had said, that I did not even hear Liz's answer. I was going to be Liz's horse! That meant that she would be my person forever. She was the person I really wanted. I was so relieved and happy that, at last, I had found a person.

Part Two

The next morning, I was grazing near the bottom gate where the dock leaves are, with a few of my friends. In the distance by the top gate, I could see a brightly coloured person walking towards us; I recognised Liz immediately. It was important that I let Liz know that I was glad that she was my person, by greeting her. I put my head up and started to walk straight to Liz.

"If you carry on eating, they'll come to you, you know." said Bobby. But I did not want to stay with my friends when Liz was in the field, so I ignored him and went to meet her. As I approached her head-on, I could see that she looked surprised, but happy, that by coming to greet her I had shown her that I knew she was now my person.

My Name

Liz said that I needed a name. I was relieved that she knew that my name was not Malcolm. Sometimes, there was a man with Liz, I liked him, but I could tell that I was probably the first horse he had met. He seemed to be a special person to Liz; his name was Ricky. I hoped that he liked me. I was very happy when Liz told me that she would call me "Cayman" and I was even happier, when she said that Ricky had thought of my name. I knew that he really did like me because this was such a good name. It made me feel important; it was as good as my great-grandfather Hercules' name. I was proud of my new name. I was proud to be Cayman.

Freeze Branding

There were some things about having a person that I did not expect. Liz seemed to worry about me a lot. I heard her say that I was "too friendly". I thought that that was strange; I liked people and if I was friendly, they were usually friendly to me. You can tell when a person is friendly because they stroke you and sometimes give you something to eat. I did not see why being friendly was a problem and anyway, I did not know how to be unfriendly.

"He's so friendly that he would follow any burly man into a lorry with 'Horse Slaughterer and Glue Boiler' written on the side !" was what Liz said. I had never seen a lorry like that, but I did not like the sound of it. I was certain that if I did see this lorry, Liz could trust me not to follow anyone into it. When Liz told me that she had arranged for me to be freeze branded, I thought that this sounded just as bad as what she was trying to protect me from.

When the lady came to do the freeze branding, Liz had already put me in a stable. A small patch of my hair was clipped off, just behind the top of my left shoulder and the lady quickly put something there which felt sharp; it did not really hurt. It was all over quickly. Liz seemed pleased when she told me that I was now '60XC', so no one would want to steal me. I was glad that she seemed satisfied, but I would not have let anyone steal me anyway, because I wanted to stay here with Liz.

Injections

Soon after I had been freeze branded, Liz told me that Sue was going to give me an injection to stop me getting flu and tetanus. I knew what an injection was; it was a sharp pain in your neck – like a bee sting. I did not think that I needed an injection.

How could I tell Liz that I could not get flu and tetanus, because I did not know how to get them? I did get the injection though.

My New Rug

As it was getting towards winter, and there was not a spare stable for me, Liz worried that I may be feeling cold. I was not cold because I had a thick coat and my mane and tail had grown longer and thicker ready for winter.

One afternoon, Liz said that she had got a new rug to keep me warm. She very carefully put the rug onto my back and slowly unfolded it so that it covered all of my back and my rump. As usual, Liz talked quietly to me; she said that she did not want the rug to frighten me. Liz did worry about some strange things. Why would I be frightened of a rug with no teeth and no claws? Once the rug was done up under my belly and across my chest, Liz stood by my head and told me very firmly:

"Cayman, this rug is the best that money can buy. We haven't got a stable yet, so I have to try to keep you warm. It was very expensive and you must not damage it, or grow out of it." I could tell that Liz meant what she said.

My new rug covered all of my body so that just my head and neck stuck out, its inside was soft and it kept me warm. It smelled strange, but I knew that if I rolled and got plenty of mud stuck to the outside, the strange smell would go; I had seen other horses do that with their new rugs.

Winter came soon and I was very glad that I had my cosy rug on. Each morning, whilst it was still dark, Liz came to check me in the field. She was always in a hurry; she said that she could not spend long with me because she had to go to work. At night, she always came back to spend longer with me.

I don't know how it happened. I was having a really good roll very early in the morning before Liz arrived and somehow I rolled myself out of my rug. As I rubbed my mane on the ground to get rid of the tickles and then got up, my rug slithered down one side of me and fell onto the ground. It just stayed there in a useless heap. I did not know what to do. I felt cold without my rug, but I remembered something worse; now it was my turn to be worried. I remembered Liz's warnings the first time she had put the rug on me. I did not think that Liz would be happy that I was no longer wearing my rug. I stood by the fence near the gate, waiting for Liz to come. I was getting colder and colder.

I was very relieved when Liz arrived. "Cayman! – where is your rug?" was the first thing she said as soon as she saw me; she looked surprised that it was no longer on my back. I knew where my rug was lying in a heap on the ground, but I needed Liz to put it on me again. I needed to show her where it was, but it was still completely dark and there was not even a moon. Liz had the long thing that shone light in her hand, so I turned and started walking across the field towards where my rug was.

"Where is your rug Cayman – are you trying to show me?" Liz must have known that I needed her to follow me because she walked after me straight away. She shone the light in her hand across the field in the direction I was walking and we could both see a dark mound on the ground. When I reached my rug, I stopped by it.

"Oh Cayman, you're so clever, you've found your rug!" Liz seemed amazed. I was glad to have my rug back on, it was so warm. As Liz did up the straps under my belly first and then across my chest, she was still telling me how clever I had been to help her find my rug in the dark. She said that it could have taken her hours to search the field and made her very late for work, if I had not helped. I thought that she was clever to know that I wanted her to follow me to where I had lost my rug. I felt lucky to have a person who could understand what I meant, because I could have been cold for a very long time. It was not long before there was a spare stable for me, so that I could go in at night. My stable was warm and I felt safe there. All of the other geldings from my field were in their stables close by. Now I had a different rug to wear in the stable at night, but Liz did not give me any warnings about that one, she just told me how smart and snug I looked in it, in my new stable.

Falling Out Of Bed

The stables had rails that slid back across the entrance, instead of doors. I had not been in my stable for many nights before I had a problem. I was lying down, but then I got myself stuck under the bottom rail. My head, neck and shoulders were outside the stable on the cold floor, but the rest of me was inside on the straw. I could not move. I did not know what to do. I felt frightened, but there was nothing I could do, so I just lay there. I was glad to hear the outside door opening. The lights went on and I knew that the lady had come to give us all our breakfast. I knew that she would help me.

"Oh Goodness Cayman! What have you done?" I was facing the wrong way to see her, but her voice sounded very surprised and I could hear her rushing away. It seemed a long time before I heard voices again. My neck and shoulder were getting very cold pressed on the floor, they felt stiff. I could lift my head, but there was no point because I needed to be able to move my shoulders and my front legs to get up and I could not do that, they were trapped.

"Oh Cay! What are you doing?" I was very relieved to hear Will's voice, but why was he asking me? I was stuck and I did not know how I got so stuck. Sam was close behind Will and then I heard the 'breakfast lady's' voice again, she still sounded very concerned:

"Oh dear! he's bound to have injured himself." Will came quietly round my head to my chest, where I could see him. Sam stayed on the other side of me:

"Good boy Cayman, easy." She slid the top rail back and tried to slide the bottom rail, but it could not move because I was stuck so tightly under it.

"We'll just have to shove him back in" Will said, "He's fallen out of bed!"

Will and Sam pushed really hard against my chest and shoulder, I felt myself move back a bit, towards the inside of my stable and the pressure of the bar went. With the next shove, I was even further back. Sam quickly slid the bottom bar away, so that I was free. My front legs felt very stiff, but I quickly got up. It was a relief to be standing up again. Sam felt my left front leg:

"He's grazed his knee and fetlock." and my left back leg:

"The side of his hock's grazed." She felt my right legs:

"He'll be alright, he just needs a bit of antiseptic where he's taken the hair off on the other side."

When Liz came to put me out in the field, Will was by my stable:

"Hello Lizzie, you won't believe what he's done! He was half in and half out of his stable, he just lay there! If it had been one of ours, it would have broken its leg."

I did feel scared when I was stuck under the rail, but I knew that eventually someone would come and help me. I never fell out of bed again because Liz put a big, strong wooden board inside the rails, in the doorway.

Later, when I was a bit older, Liz's mother, who is 'Mrs B.', put me out in the mornings. I still had my breakfast early and then I would wait for Mrs B.. It was noisy in the stables with the other horses having their rugs changed and being put out. But, despite everything that was going on all around me, I usually lay down again for another snooze until Mrs B. arrived. I felt content and safe in my stable.

Liz told people: "If he could talk, what he would say most often is: 'Oh, alright then!' He really isn't bothered by very much."

She was right.

'I *had* to find a person'

Chapter Four

BEING RIDDEN

I was a real 'riding horse'! Now that Liz was my person, we went out for rides. I thought that my mother would be very proud of me. Sometimes being ridden was hard work. The farmer's daughter at my farm on Anglesey had only taken me for short rides round some fields close to my own field and we had only walked and trotted. Now it seemed that Liz wanted to go everywhere. We went far away from my field and I was afraid that I would not be able to find my way back. To start with I got very tired. Although I was strong and hardly felt Liz's weight on my back, I had to think more than ever before and that made me feel tired.

The first time Liz took me to 'Long Hattons', it seemed so far that I was worried that I might never see my field again. 'Long Hattons' was the first place where I ever cantered with Liz on my back. When she asked me to canter by the hedge up the side of a big field, I was not sure whether I was really allowed to canter with a person on my back. As it seemed to be what Liz wanted, I started to canter, but it felt strange, so I trotted again. I thought that trotting was fast enough; I did not want Liz to fall off my back because she might hurt herself. I knew that as a 'riding horse' I should look after my rider. I was surprised when Liz urged me on again – she really did want me to canter. I did a very slow canter so that Liz would be safe, but we did not seem to be getting anywhere. The field was very big and it went up hill, it was hard work. My back legs and haunches ached already and I felt a bit out of breath, so I trotted again. I was sure that Liz must be mistaken and that horses were not really supposed to canter all the way up big fields like this, with riders on their backs. Liz let me walk for a while and I felt better, she told me that as I was young, I did not have to do too much.

As I got older and stronger, our rides got longer and longer. 'Long Hattons' became one of our shortest rides and I usually galloped up the field that I could not canter up when I was only three!

Liz's First Fall

The first time that Liz and I went for a ride with Liz's mother, 'Mrs B.', and Corris, was the first time that Liz fell off me.

Corris was the dominant gelding in our field. Although

he was smaller than me, he was twelve years older and was so clever that he had already done *everything* that a horse could do. I was a bit frightened of him. I tried hard for the whole ride to do everything right. As we were coming home, just after Chillington Hall, Corris cantered along a wide grass verge. As the grass verge got narrower and steeper, he kept on cantering, effortlessly. When I tried to do the same, my legs got tangled up and I slipped on the muddy, steep part of the verge. I felt Liz's weight on my neck, not on the saddle; because that felt funny, I bucked. Liz slid down my shoulder and I stepped over her as she lay on the road. I was very surprised, everything happened so quickly.

I was frightened that Liz would be cross with me for making her fall off my back.

I ate some grass whilst I wondered what to do next. I was relieved when Liz sat up, she then stood up and hopped towards me; she had gone very lame on her left leg, she did not seem to be able to put it on the ground. Liz got onto my back by climbing up a gate. She told Mrs B that her left ankle was hurting a lot. Corris told me that this was my fault because he had cantered on the same verge and Mrs B had stayed on his back.

Liz did not get cross with me; instead she stroked my neck and said:

"I'm sorry Cayman, that was my fault for asking a horse as big as you to canter on such a soft grass verge." I was confused, I did not know whose fault it was, but I did know that I was sorry that Liz had been hurt.

Liz's Second Fall

The horses in my field were divided into those who would go over the motorway bridge and those who would not; although some of the ones who would not said that this was because their people were frightened, not them.

When Liz said that she was going to show me the motorway bridge I was curious.

It was close to the stables. We went up the hill with the farm on top, down the other side, and there it was. Liz let me stand at the start of the bridge from where I could see down onto a huge road below. She said that as it was Sunday and still early, the road would be quiet. I did not think that it was quiet at all. Every so often a shiny thing would dart along it unexpectedly, making a rumbling and 'whooshing' sound. Sometimes the shiny things chased each other. I was not frightened, but I did think that the huge road was strange and that I should be on my guard.

After Liz had shown me the motorway bridge a few times and she could tell that I was not frightened, she rode me over it. Liz explained:

"The rides on the other side of the bridge are wonderful! Even if you feel unsure, you'll see that it will be worthwhile to cross the bridge."

The first time Liz rode me over the bridge, she encouraged me by talking quietly to me all the time. I could feel how hard she was concentrating and looking straight across to the other side; that helped me to trust her, even when I was walking across the middle, where we were no longer on 'the stables side' but not quite on 'the lovely rides side'. When we were right across the bridge I could feel how relieved Liz was, she stroked me a lot and praised me.

On our rides we went over the bridge quite often, and I began to feel brave. But then, one afternoon in winter when it was raining and starting to get dark, we were going over the bridge, but the sounds were different. I could hear something hissing like a snake and flapping; the rumbling was louder than usual. All I could see of the darting things was their eyes which dazzled me. When we were in the middle of the bridge, no longer on 'the lovely rides side' and not quite on 'the stables side', I became very, *very* frightened.

I started to trot, but then I was cantering. I quickly reached 'the stables side' of the bridge, but I could still hear the hissing and flapping sounds and the loud rumbling.

I was cantering faster and faster, up the hill. I could feel the stirrup irons knocking against my shoulders and my sides; that frightened me more and made me go even faster.

I knew that Liz was still on my back but I was not listening to her, all I could think of was getting away from the dangerous bridge and home to the safety of my stable as quickly as possible. I was galloping. Past the farm, and down the steep hill on the other side. I could hear Liz telling me to "Wooah", but her voice sounded shaky. I did not slow down.

Although I was going very fast, it seemed as if my vulnerable back end was trailing along way behind. If only I were not so long! I was *sure* that the hissing, flapping things were chasing me, getting closer and closer. I could feel their hot breath around my back legs as they were about to pounce onto my rump, drag me down and rip big chunks from my flesh with the fangs which I knew they must have in their open jaws. I was terrified.

At the bottom of the hill, the lane is blocked by a five-barred gate right across it. At the side of that gate there is another, narrow gate, which is the one that we usually went through to get home. As I hurtled onto the grass verge and aimed for the narrow gate, I saw in the gloom that it was closed. It was too tall to jump; we would be trapped. My whole weight was propelling me nearer and nearer to the closed gate.

I had to put *all* of my effort into stopping. The soft ground helped me to slow down, but I still only just managed to stop before I got to the gate. As I did so, I realised that I could no longer hear the hissing, flapping things – they had vanished. What a relief! We were safe!

Going from gallop to stop was too much for Liz though, she rolled over my left shoulder onto the soft, wet ground. She landed on her feet, but immediately sat down on the grass in front of me. Her face looked strange, it was not bright and shiny as usual, it looked very, very pale. I decided that I had definitely done the right thing in running away from the dangerous motorway bridge as Liz had obviously been frightened by it too.

Liz led me into my stable, Mrs B was there and Liz told her what had happened. Liz took off my tack, put on my rug and was about to lead me out to the field, when Mrs B said:

"Why are you turning him out in his stable rug?" Mrs B helped put on my turn-out rug and then said to Liz:

"I think you're a bit shocked – I'll put him out." As I walked down the lane with Mrs B, I could not understand why I had not been praised for saving Liz from the dangerous motorway bridge.

Liz's Third Fall

The next time Liz tacked me up for a ride, she told me:

"Cayman, I've 'lost my nerve', we are going out with Corris and Mrs B and we are *only going to walk*." I did not mind walking at all. I did not know what Liz meant when she said she had 'lost her nerve', but it sounded as if it was something she needed, so I hoped she found it again soon. I thought she probably would because I heard Will say to her:

"Never mind Chuck – it'll come back!"

We went for a very long ride, at a walk. Corris got fed up with walking and jogged sometimes, but I was quite happy to walk. We were coming home up the back road, near to the stables, when we had to walk through an enormous puddle that went right across the road, before the corner. I was not at all afraid of water, so I carried on walking.

I was in the middle of the puddle when suddenly something that I could not see jumped out of the water and bit my belly. I didn't know how it happened, but my head went down between my front legs, my back arched and I shot upwards. I landed on all four feet at the same time and trotted out of the puddle as fast as I could. It was then that I realised that my back felt different, I could not feel Liz on it. As I trotted towards the corner I put my head up high so that I could see behind me. I was surprised to see Liz sitting in the puddle in the middle of the road, holding her elbow. I could easily have carried on trotting back into the stable yard, but as I thought that this might have something to do with me, I slowed down and walked into the big gateway on the corner.

Whilst I grazed, I kept an eye on Liz who was walking up the road towards me. I thought about running to my stable, but as she did not really look cross, I stayed in the gateway. As I put my head up, Liz said:

"Wooah! Cayman, stand still." She took hold of my reins and positioned me so that she could get onto my back from the gate. When she was on me again, she stroked my neck. Usually we came home with the reins long so that I could stretch my neck, but this time Liz made the bit press the corners of my mouth all the way home. I could tell that she was not very happy with me because she did not talk to me as much as usual. I felt sorry that I had made her sit in the big puddle.

A few days later Liz told me that she was afraid that I would buck her off my back again, so Will was going to ride me, to make sure that I was safe. I did not mind Will riding me, I liked Will, but I was worried that Liz thought that I might not be safe. I was worried that I was not very good at being 'a riding horse' and that my mother would not be proud of me. How could I explain to Liz that I had only bucked because something had jumped out of the puddle and bitten my belly and that I would never throw her off my back on purpose?

So, we went for a ride. Will rode me and Liz rode a bay mare whom I did not know. It seemed strange to see Liz on another horse, I felt sorry that she was not riding me and I was worried that she might not want to be my person anymore. I tried as hard as I could to do everything right. As we rode along Will said to Liz:

"You know, what it probably was, was some water splashing up under his belly. You just need to keep his head up." So that was what bit my belly – water! I knew that water was not something to be frightened of; Will was clever.

When we got back to the yard, Alison was there. Liz told her that Will said that she needed to keep my head up. Alison laughed: "You need some 'daisy reins', but they're usually for little fat ponies, to stop them putting their heads down to graze. I don't think you can get them for 17hh horses!" I was insulted by the sound of 'daisy reins'. I had to let Liz know that she could trust me, *without* 'daisy reins'.

Lungeing

Things got worse. Liz said that as she really had 'lost her nerve', she would lunge me instead of riding me. She took me into the big building with lights and a soft floor. I remembered what to do and for a while everything went well, I walked, trotted and halted when Liz asked me to, but it was not very interesting and now that I was four, I seemed to have so much energy.

My friends in the field had shown me how to play some new games and I thought that Liz might like these games too. My favourite game was rearing up and pawing the air with my front legs. I was so good at this that I could also walk forward a few paces on my back legs at the same time. So, just when I thought Liz might be getting a bit bored with lungeing me, I jumped up onto my back legs and walked towards her, pawing the air with my front legs. Liz looked very surprised, she walked backwards away from me. I lost my balance and was back on four legs again, but I was so keen to show Liz how much fun this game was, that I quickly reared up once more and very cleverly walked towards Liz on my back legs, whilst I pawed the air with my front legs. I wanted Liz to join in, but she obviously did not know the game at all because she was still walking backwards away from me. I wobbled and was back on four legs. I stood still, feeling proud of myself for knowing such a clever game. As Liz came up to me, she looked frightened, like she did when I saved her from the dangerous motorway bridge. I do not think that she liked my game. We did not do any more lungeing that day.

Sam

The next day, I got a big surprise when Sam came into my stable. Sam did not usually handle me; I wondered whether she was going to ride me. Sam put on my saddle and bridle, but when she also put on the other bridle with the thick, tight noseband with metal rings on it, I realised that this meant that Sam was going to lunge me. She led me into the big building and asked me to walk – and then trot – on the lunge, which I did. The trouble was that I was so full of games; they were wriggling around inside me – it was hard not to let them out. As I was going round and round, my favourite game was wriggling too much for me to ignore. I decided that perhaps Sam would appreciate how clever my rearing game was. She certainly seemed to know what she was doing, so she may know this game too. It was easy to jump onto my back legs; I was just starting to paw the air with my front legs, and thinking how much fun this was, when Sam let out the loudest, most terrifying roar. I did not know that a person could make such a frightening noise, I had certainly never heard one do it before – I had never been roared at in my life. I was so astonished that I immediately dropped back onto four legs and stood frozen, looking at Sam with my head high and my eyes wide. I did not know what to do. I was afraid that Sam might roar again. I wanted to run away, but I was too scared to move. As Sam walked up to me, she looked *very, very* angry.

"You needn't think you're going to do that with me!" she growled. I felt very frightened. Sam made me bend my neck, so that she could clip reins onto my bit. I had already decided that I would do *everything* she wanted; her roaring had hurt my ears. Sam made me walk, trot and canter for a long time, but I did not dare be disobedient. Eventually she told me to halt. I was tired and out of breath. I was glad that it was over. Sam unclipped the lunge line and walked away; she left the big building and closed the door firmly behind her. I was alone but I still had all of my tack on. Usually my tack was taken off when I had finished. As I stood in the corner of the building, trying to work out what was happening, it dawned on me that as my tack was still on, this must mean that Sam had not finished with me. I felt unhappy, I was frightened, but I could not escape, I just had to stay in the big building and wait to see what happened next. There was not even anything for me to eat.

After a long time, the door opened, I must have been dozing because it startled me. Sam clipped the lunge line back onto my noseband and set me off again at a brisk walk.

I was desperate to show her that I would never be naughty again. As Sam asked me to trot on, I used all my effort to do exactly what she wanted. I think that Sam could tell how hard I was trying because after I had trotted round a few times, she let me walk, then halt. I was very relieved when she said:

"Alright Cayman that'll do." I decided that I definitely would *never* try to play rearing games with people again.

Police Horse

Although Liz was still looking after me, she had stopped riding me and she did not lunge me. I was very surprised when she told me:

"Cayman, I've decided to sell you to the police." That was the worst thing I could have heard. At first I did not believe what Liz had said. Liz could not sell me, she was my person, she could not send me away. I was very unhappy. Liz explained:

"I've only contacted police forces in areas that I think would be nice for you; there is one area where they only have grey horses, and they're interested in you." I did not understand what 'the police' was, but even if it was where grey horses went, I was not going. I was *not* going to leave Liz.

Liz told me that she was going away to the Cayman Islands and that when she got back she would sort out what was going to happen to me. That was very confusing. It sounded as if *I* should be going to the Cayman Islands, I was 'Cayman' after all, not Liz, so why was she going there? but anyway, I did not want either of us *ever* to go away.

As it was summer, I stayed in my field; I did all of the things I usually did, but even playing rearing games with my friends did not make me feel happy. Liz had gone away, I did not know when she would come back and I was to be sold. I was miserable.

After a long time, when I was grazing at the top end of the

field, near the stream, I thought that I caught sight of a person I recognised. I quickly put my head up to see better. I could not believe my eyes, it was Liz with Ricky, they were on the opposite side of the field, on the lane. I was so relieved to see Liz that I let out a very loud whinny and immediately trotted straight across the field towards her. Liz got through the fence and was walking quickly towards me. When I was close enough, I could see that she looked very happy to see me. As Liz put her arms up tightly around each side of my neck and pressed her head against me, I could tell that she had decided that she would be my person forever. Liz rode me again and this time, I made a very special effort to look after her. I *never* wanted to risk being sent away again.

Monty Roberts

When I was five, Liz told me that she was going to see a demonstration by a man called Monty Roberts who understands horses. I am glad that she did that, because what she saw changed the way that Liz behaved towards me. Liz had always been kind to me and sometimes, like when I lost my rug in the dark field, I was surprised how well she understood what I tried to tell her. Liz told Mrs B.:

"Seeing Monty Roberts was like an evangelical experience! Instead of trying to dominate Cayman, I will try harder to understand him, now that I realise that sometimes he is 'a frightened little mouse trapped in a big horse's body'."

Liz and I got on better and better as we did more together. Liz said that riding enabled her to enjoy the countryside. We went everywhere in all seasons and all weathers. We trusted each other, which made whatever we did easier. We got to know and understand each other so well that we often knew what each other was thinking.

Trust

Because we trusted each other Liz let me do some unusual things; one was 'mad trotting', which I started to do when I was about eight. I only did 'mad trotting' coming home and I always did it in certain places, such as up Chillington Lane, to the farm on the corner with all of the interesting animals, or from the first bend in the lane after Chillington Hall. Liz said that she thought that I might be 'pacing', because all she could do was wobble from side to side in the saddle whilst I flew along, at the speed of a fast canter, my feet hardly touching the ground.

Liz joked that if I had been doing my ancestors' job as a carthorse pulling a coal cart, all the loose coal would have flown off the back of the cart and been strewn along the road behind me, or if I was pulling a cart carrying churns, all of the milk would have turned to butter. Liz always let me do 'mad trotting' and I know that she enjoyed it because sometimes, over the noise of my hooves, I could hear her laughing.

Liz also trusted me to scratch behind my ear with my back

hoof whilst she was sitting on me. This meant that I had to be very balanced as I brought my head and neck round towards my back end and my back leg forward; they met in the middle, just about where Liz's leg was. What Liz forgot was that it was *me* who had to trust *her*, not to upset my delicate balance, whilst I was scratching behind my ear.

When I was about eleven, Liz went to Lisa's to ride Velvet in the way that Lisa rode her. When Liz came back, she told me:

"Cayman, I'm going to ride you in a different way. I'm going to stop doing all the thinking for you. You have to start to think for yourself. *You're* the horse, not me, they're *your* legs, you should be in control of where you put them!" I could not really disagree and I did sometimes think that Liz tried too hard anyway. It sounded as though she was going to try to be more relaxed, which would mean that I could relax too, I thought that was a good idea.

When Liz tried this new way of riding me I liked it. She sat lighter in the saddle and I could feel that she held the reins in one hand, she was more relaxed. I quickly got used to balancing myself, just like when I played in the field. I felt that I could go more freely; it was enjoyable being ridden like this – and because Liz had to trust me to think for myself, that strengthened the bond between us. Once Liz learned this way of riding, we had some of our best ever rides.

A 'real riding horse'

Chapter Five

GAMES

*A*fter I had come to Gunstone and Liz had become my person, I felt so settled and happy that I wanted to play games a lot of the time. There were so many horses in the geldings' field that there was always someone to play with and sometimes lots of us would feel like a game at the same time.

These are my favourite games ...

The Spooky Game

When the weather was windy in autumn it made us feel spooky. We would be a bit frightened by the slightest thing, such as some leaves blowing up into the air. But, because we felt like a game, we would make our eyes wide, put our heads and tails up high, snort and pretend to be a lot more frightened than we really were. Even if just one of us did this, others would see and do the same, so that eventually lots of us were playing 'The Spooky Game'; that made the danger seem more real, which made us even more spooky. By the time our people came to get us in, we could all have convinced ourselves that our field and the lane to the yard were so full of things to spook at, that we could be quite difficult to lead.

In spring, as the weather became warmer and the new grass grew, we all felt playful. Even the very old horses, whose painful joints made it difficult for them to get up and lie down, would forget that they were no longer young, shake their manes and trot with short stiff strides across the field, then stand sniffing the warm air which carried the promise of summer and long hot days for grazing lazily on lush grass. We all had more energy when spring came.

Starting a Game

There are a few ways of starting a game. When I was very young, about three or four, I usually tried to start a game by going up behind another horse, nipping his rump hard with my front teeth and then waiting for him to do something playful. When this worked, the other horse would often do a 'play buck', which is where you buck, but do not stretch-out your back legs, so that no one gets hurt. I would try to nip his flanks and, by this time, he would be trying to nip me too. Next, we would try to nip each other's shoulders, necks and chests; it was really good fun if one of us then tried to escape and we both ran across the field together, still nipping at each other. Sometimes though, my attempt to start a game did not work so well. If the horse whose rump I nipped was too old to play, or too grumpy, or just wanted to be left in peace to graze, then he would tell me to get lost by kicking. I got kicked a lot!

Jerry

Once, I got such a bad kick to the top of my left leg, that when Liz came to get me in, my leg had swollen-up so that it was double its normal size; the skin felt stretched and hot – it really hurt. I was relieved to see Liz, she always sorted things out. Liz said that she would call the vet, but the vet who came was not Sue, my usual vet, it was Jerry.

This was the first time that I had seen Jerry. As he came into my stable, quietly and gently, he greeted me:

"Hello little friend." I liked Jerry immediately, because he had come to help me, and he knew that although I was 17hh, I really was little, *inside.*

Jerry must have been the same sort of vet as Sue, because he gave me an injection in my neck, just like Sue did; he also showed Liz how to put a long thin tube into my leg and squirt water into it, to clean it inside. Liz had to do this every day and I had to live in a small paddock, by myself, whilst my leg got better, so that I could not try to play with any other horses and get kicked again.

As soon as my leg was better, I went back into the geldings' field with my friends.

It was good to be back, and of course I wanted to play! I don't think that I had learned my lesson, because it was not long before I annoyed another horse and got another bad kick; this time, my right shoulder swelled up. Jerry gave me another injection. Liz said that she was fed up with having to pay vet's bills because I was too silly to get out of the way of horses who wanted to kick me. Liz probably did have a point. Anyway, each time I got a bad kick and was lame, I could not be ridden, so Liz and I could not have so much fun.

There were lots more kicks which hurt me, but did not make me lame. Liz also knew about those, because every night when she got me in, she felt my legs and looked all over me for injuries. Even if I had just a tiny cut from a kick, Liz always noticed it.

Pony Dragging

Liz was not very impressed by my behaviour. I wanted to impress her, so I decided to try to avoid getting kicked by being more careful who I started a game with, and by biting them and then running away immediately, so that I was out of reach of their back legs. Also, I tried out new ways of starting a game. I found that I could start a game by nipping shoulders, necks and chests instead of rumps; that was safer. Or, if a pony was wearing a head collar, I could easily grab the head collar in my mouth and drag the pony around the field; no one in the field was bigger and stronger than me, so they had no choice! George and Rupert were my size, but they were much older than me, they lived in stables next to each other and always grazed together, they did not usually play.

There were plenty of ponies with head collars to choose from. Some were so naughty to catch, that their people attached short pieces of rope to their head collars. I could grab the dangling rope with my teeth, and once I had it, my game of 'pony dragging' was even more fun! I did not hurt the ponies and they must have enjoyed it too, because everyone was still my friend.

Nipping Liz

Another really funny game was nipping Liz's bottom; I did this when she bent over to pick out my front feet. I knew that it was naughty, because when I was three and Liz became my person, she had trained me not to do it, by very sternly saying:

"Cayman, No!" and pushing my head away each time I tried; but when I was older I did it for a joke.

Liz knew that I knew it was a naughty thing to do, she also knew that I thought it was funny ... she thought it was funny too, but sometimes I did hurt her by mistake. I knew when I had hurt her because she would make a sudden sharp noise which surprised my ears.

In August, when I was twelve, I heard Liz say to Mrs B. that she had had to explain to a nurse why she had five bruises on the left side of her body. They were all caused by me. As it had been very hot, Liz had worn shorts or even dresses instead of her usual thick trousers when she had handled me. When I had nipped her for a joke, as she did my front feet, I had left big bruises on the top of her left leg and on her bottom. There was also another very big bruise lower down her left leg, where we got our legs tangled up as she was leading me up the lane, one hot evening when she wore a dress. By mistake, I had also caught the tip of my front hoof on the top of Liz's foot and once, when I was impatient, I had nipped the top of my arm because she was standing outside my stable talking to Mrs B. and ignoring me. That made five bruises. Liz said that the nurse probably thought that she lived with a violent man, but she had explained that all of her injuries were caused by me, and that she did not mind.

When Leah, Sooty's person – who is four – was at the stables, Liz would ask her to help. Leah would stand on the other side of the rails, facing me and, whilst Liz was doing my front feet, if Leah saw me start to swing my head round to nip Liz's bottom, Liz told her to shout:

"Cayman, NO!" That would surprise me and I would swing my head back to look at Leah. I could tell that Leah took the responsibility which Liz gave her very seriously. So, to make it even funnier for everyone, I added another game, which was 'teasing Leah'. I would deliberately start to swing my head round as if I was going to nip Liz, but just as I could see Leah taking a deep breath to shout:

"Cayman, NO!" I would swing my head back to her; Leah did not know whether to shout at me or not. I could do this a few times whilst Liz was picking my front feet. Liz did not get her bottom nipped and Leah was still my friend, even if she was a bit confused; it was very funny.

Just once, when I was about seven, I did the funniest joke of all on Liz. It was early in the morning in the summer, and as usual, Liz was picking out my feet, before turning me out. Whilst she was bending over, I swung my head round, intending to nibble her back, which is a friendly thing that horses do to each other; it does not hurt and I thought that Liz would like it. As I gently closed my front teeth, I felt that instead of Liz's shirt, I had the thick leather strap that she wore round her middle in my teeth. It felt like a head collar ... that reminded me of the game of 'pony dragging'. I thought that Liz may not like it if I dragged her and anyway, my stable was too small. But, with the thick leather strap between my teeth, I did feel like doing something funny, so I clamped my front teeth shut as hard as I could, tensed my jaw and my chest and braced my front legs as I lifted my head, with my teeth still clamped onto the strap round Liz's middle. As I felt her weight, I tensed my back and my haunches and continued to lift my head higher, so that Liz was off the ground.

My joke worked! Liz's voice sounded as if she could not believe what was happening as she said:

"Cayman! Put me down!" Steadily, I lowered my head and neck until Liz's feet were back on the floor, then I released my grip on the thick leather strap, so that she was free. Liz looked at me with her eyes wide, she was smiling a lot as she said: "Cayman! That was NOT funny!" but I could tell that *really,* she thought that it was *very* funny.

It was usually me who played jokes on Liz. I don't think that people like jokes as much as horses do, but once I did get a joke played on me. After breakfast, Liz had groomed me and I knew that we were going for a ride because she had put my saddle on the box outside Bobby's stable as usual; but then she got distracted by Mrs B.; they were talking, right outside my stable and ignoring me. I was impatient to get going so, as my weaving gate was not across the entrance to my stable, I reached my neck out over the top rail and, with my teeth, pulled the big towel that Liz dried her hands on, off the bar on the outside wall. To get Liz's attention, I threw the towel at her feet. Liz said crossly:

"Cayman! *don't do that!*" before she picked up the towel, put it back on the bar and carried on talking. I was determined to get Liz to pay attention to me, so I pulled the towel off the bar with my teeth and threw it on to the ground again.

"Cayman!" Liz sounded annoyed. As she picked up the towel, I heard her say to Mrs B.:

"I'm going to try something ... " Then Liz threw the towel at me! I was surprised, but I didn't step back. It slid down my nose onto the ground in front of me. Liz quickly retrieved it and threw it again, this time she threw it higher.

The towel landed over my ears and stayed on my head, covering my eyes and my whole face, right down to the end of my nose. I didn't mind, it smelled of my stable. At least I had Liz's attention; she obviously thought that her joke was funny, she was laughing as she took the towel off my head:

"Most horses would have been frightened by that – you're so good Cayman." Liz had stopped talking to Mrs B. and started to put on my saddle; at last we could get going.

The Galloping Game

The best game of all was when everyone in the geldings' field joined in 'The Galloping Game'. Sometimes I started the game, sometimes someone else started it. First one horse would begin to gallop round the field; others would see him and join in so that very quickly, there was no one left grazing and we were all galloping in a herd. There were usually about twenty-three of us in our field, which was very big. Everyone found their place. It was very exciting: the biggest fastest horses like me led, then came the smaller faster horses, the bigger slower horses and the smaller slower ones. Horses who were very old, or lame, joined in right at the back.

Even George played 'The Galloping Game'. George is Rupert's friend, he is the same size as me. George had been a steeplechaser – he was bred to run in The Grand National, but he had a very bad injury, so he could not race any more. He was not ridden and did not often canter in the field, but when we played 'The Galloping Game', the excitement made George feel like a young steeplechaser again. He joined in as enthusiastically as everyone else and he was *never* at the back. 'The Galloping Game' was good for us all because it made us so happy.

Liz and Mrs B. saw 'The Galloping Game' once when they came to get Corris and me in. Afterwards, I heard Liz tell Karen, George's person, about it, Liz was very impressed.

Liz said that as she and Mrs B. approached the gateway, they could not see any horses in the field, which they thought was strange, but then, as they got nearer, they could hear the thunder of our hooves as we galloped round the far corner, near the allotments and along the Brewood Road side of the field, before turning to come up the side by the lane.

Liz said that I was leading and that I looked magnificent, with the whole herd fanning out behind me. She said that I was galloping so fast that I did not notice her and Mrs B. standing on the other side of the gate. (They had stayed outside the field for safety.) She watched us gallop off up the field, turn along the lakeside and again at the far side, before galloping down towards the Brewood Road again.

I did see Liz and Mrs B. by the gate as we thundered up the field again, but although I knew that Liz was there and turned my head to look at her as we all charged past, I was going *much too fast* to stop. I felt as if I was being pushed on by the whole herd behind me.

The next time we came up the field, I decided that I

should try to get to the gateway to meet Liz, but it was not easy as we all seemed to be moving so fast that our own speed kept us together. As we got level with the gate, at full gallop, I concentrated really hard and managed to pull myself away from the herd, which continued on up the field. I had a shock when I realised that the gate was much closer than I expected, and I was still galloping because that was what my legs had got used to doing. It was a good job that Liz and Mrs B. were on the other side of the gate. I threw my weight back as far as I could, stuck my front legs out in front of me, drew my neck up and back, and braced myself for hitting the gate. As I slid to a halt, still with my front legs stuck out in front of me, I could not believe that the gate was still in one piece, *very close* to my neck. Liz and Mrs B. must have expected me to come crashing through the gate, because they were standing well back from their side of it, looking surprised. I had no energy left to do anything but stand still, with sweat dripping off me, my sides heaving, trying to get my breath back.

Liz came into the field, she lifted-up my forelock and tried to rub my forehead, but it was so wet that her hand just slipped about. Stroking my neck was no better; there was not a single part of me that was dry. As Liz was putting on my head collar, Corris came trotting up to the gate. Although he was also covered in sweat and breathing heavily, he approached Liz and Mrs B. in a much more controlled way than I had, and the gate itself was certainly in no danger.

Liz asked me:

"Have you been having fun Cayman?" It always seemed to make Liz happy when she knew that I had enjoyed myself. She smiled at me in a way which meant that although she thought that I was a bit silly, she was also very proud of me. Liz knew that the best game of all was 'The Galloping Game'.

'There was always someone to play with'

Chapter Six

SHOES, FEET AND LEGS

*P*eople always noticed my feet, especially my front feet, which were very big because my great grandfather Hercules was a Shire horse. When Liz became my person, one of the first things she did was to have my feet trimmed by Ian the farrier. Ian seemed to be as big as me, and probably even stronger; he was very gentle and I did not mind having my feet done, afterwards they felt light and neat. Alison from Anglesey was in the yard when my feet were first trimmed. I think that she could tell that I was surprised to see her again; she was obviously surprised by my feet. She said:

"Yes Cayman, it's your Auntie Alison! Now who's got pony toes?" I liked my new feet.

To start with, Liz rode me without shoes, but as we went further and further on the road, my front feet, which were wider and flatter than the back ones, started to get sore, so Ian put shoes on just my front feet. I did not mind being shod for the first time because I trusted Ian, but what was strange was the noise that my front feet made on the yard and on the road. The noise always went where I went and even if I lifted my feet up very high, I could not get away from it.

When I was four I had my first full set of shoes on all of my feet. Because I was so big, and my feet made such a loud 'clip-clopping' sound, everyone knew that it was me coming into the yard. Liz said that they would say: "That sounds like Cayman!" even before they could see me.

My First Operation at Newmarket

My shoes could give me problems though. Once, in the night, when I was five, I trod on the inside of my right front shoe with the inside of my left front shoe, and made it so loose that it slipped across under my foot. When I put my weight on my right foot again, the sharpest pain I have ever felt shot through the sole of my foot, right up my leg. I instantly took my weight off my right foot by leaning backwards, with my weight on my back legs and my right leg stretched out in front of me. All I could do was stay like that and wait for Liz to come and help me.

I was very relieved to see Liz in the morning. Liz knew immediately, by the way I was standing, that there was something *very* wrong with me. She came quietly into the stable and picked up my right foot, she tried to move the shoe with her hand but it would not move. Liz put my foot down carefully, she stroked my neck:

"It's alright boy, Ian will be here soon." I could tell by her voice that Liz thought that this was something serious, she sounded worried.

I did not have to wait long before Ian came and pulled all of my old shoes off. He said that one of the nails had stuck into my sole. I was glad to be able to stand properly on all four feet again. Then Jerry, one of the vets, arrived, because his horse also lived at Gunstone. Jerry gave me two injections in my neck and gave Liz some medicine to put in my food. As Ian re-shod me, Liz still sounded worried:

"It's exactly six weeks since he was last shod; when I left him last night all of his shoes were on securely, it's not fair that he's got a pricked sole."

Liz said that I might feel a bit poorly because I had had injections, so she would turn me out to graze rather than taking me for a ride. I was sorry that we were not going for a ride as it was a lovely bright morning, but I always enjoyed going out to graze. As I started grazing I did not think about my right foot, but it soon started to hurt me. By the time Liz came to get me in, it hurt more, and when we walked up the lane I tried not to put my weight on it. Liz could see that I was still very lame; she told me that she would ask Jerry to help me.

The next day, both Jerry *and* Ian came to help me. As I was trotted-up in the yard, I was still lame on my front right foot. Ian pulled the new shoe off and I could feel him cutting into the sole of my foot, but that did not hurt me. Jerry then put something which smelled strong into my foot, bandaged it up and put some shiny tape over the bandage. He said that I had to go into my stable and stay there.

To start with, I did not mind being in because I had plenty of haylage and there was usually something going on either in my block of stables or in the yard outside, so there was always something to listen to and often something to watch. I had a window in the back wall of my stable so I could look out onto the lane that goes up the hill. I could also see the house where Rupert's person, who is also called Liz, lives. Sometimes Skunk, who is a black cat with white paws, would come to talk to me, he was my friend.

Liz came early every morning to change the bandage on my foot. I got very good at having the old bandage cut off, my sole cleaned, a new pad bandaged on and my whole foot wrapped up in strips of shiny tape, without putting my foot down onto my bedding even once.

Every few days, Jerry would come to see me and I would be trotted up on the yard, but I was still lame. I got *very* bored. I did have a straw bed but I started eating that in between nets of haylage. Liz said that as I could not digest straw, I might get all blocked up inside and end up with colic, so she would have to change my bedding to wood shavings, which I could not eat. Liz took all of the straw away. She did not like wasting anything so she gave what was clean to Mrs B. for Corris's bed and the rest went on the muck heap, then she put down eight bales of wood shavings. Whilst Liz did this, I waited in Corris's stable. I always liked going into other horses' stables because it gave me a chance to see whether they had left any food which I could eat. I searched his stable thoroughly, but Corris had not left anything.

When the dust from the wood shavings had settled, Liz took me back into my own stable. I hardly recognised it, there was a new bright bed, which looked like deep snow.

As I put my muzzle into the wood shavings, they went up my nostrils and stuck to my whiskers, I had to snort to get rid of them. Liz could see that I was curious about my new bed, but she sounded quite stern when she told me:

"Cayman, with what I've spent on your bed, I could have bought a new quilt for my own bed, DO NOT mess it up!" I was happy that Liz had given me such an inviting, comfortable-looking bed, I did not mind that I could not eat it.

Despite having the best bed in my stable block, my foot was still not getting better. Jerry said that I needed to have my foot x-rayed. Liz reassured me that this was a picture of my bones and it would not hurt. The picture was sent to a vet in Newmarket. Liz told me that he said I had a chipped pedal bone, which was infected, and I needed an operation.

Very early in the morning, when it was still dark, Liz came into my stable, she said that we were going to Newmarket so that I could have an operation to make my foot better. As I ate my breakfast, Liz put a bandage on my tail. When I had finished she led me out into the yard. The lorry was in the middle of the yard with the ramp down and Will was there. Will called out to Liz:

"We need to get off as quick as we can, so we don't get stuck in the traffic on the motorway; it'd be best if I loaded him, we don't want him mucking about." As Will took my lead rope, I put my head up high and tried to see into the lorry, but it was too dark to see clearly. Will gave the rope a tug from which I knew that there was only one thing I could do, and that was go up the ramp with him, into the lorry. As soon as I started walking forwards with Will, I felt safe. I was tied-up in the lorry, eating from the haylage net in no time. The engine started up and the lorry pulled forwards and rocked from side to side as I got my balance and settled down to eat again.

Eventually, we seemed to be going fast, on a very smooth road. As it got lighter and lighter outside and I could see more clearly out of the tiny window in front of me. I got really scared. There were things darting past the lorry low down, but sometimes a bigger, higher thing would pass, very close to me. There was nothing I could do to get away as I was tied up right by the window. I had not seen anything like this when I came from Anglesey in the low trailer with Dewi. I was alone and very frightened.

After a long time, we seemed to slow down, turn and go in a different direction. Then the lorry stopped. I could see cars and lorries on the ground but they were either standing still or only moving very slowly. When a door in front of where I was standing opened and I saw Liz, I was so relieved that I did a huge shrill neigh, which was one that I only did when I had been *very* frightened. As Liz held out a big carrot for me to bite, she smiled at me in a way that told me that she understood that I had been very frightened.

I took such big bites of the carrot that Liz could tell that, although it was nice to have a carrot, I was not really concentrating on eating it politely, like I usually did. Liz did not come into my part of the lorry but she reassured me by stroking my neck over the rail:

"It's alright Cayman, nothing is going to hurt you, we'll soon be there, don't worry."

Liz did not sound at all worried and the big carrot had made me feel better.

As the lorry started up again and Liz went off, I did not feel so frightened. I did not know where Liz had gone, but I thought that she would not be far away and would probably reappear when we got to where we were going. Getting up so early and being so frightened had made me tired. I had eaten a lot of haylage and the sound of the lorry rumbling along made me feel sleepy. As I lowered my head, I was not looking out of the window any longer, so I felt more settled. I went to sleep for a while. I only woke up when the lorry seemed to be chugging very slowly up somewhere narrow. Out of the window I could see a wall going past and we seemed to be going backwards. I could hear that the lorry was going over something which made a crunching sound, and then it stopped. The ramp went down slowly, then I heard Will's voice behind me:

"Alright Cayman (I was glad he had stopped calling me 'Malcolm'!) let's get you out."

Will quickly untied my rope and led me steadily down the ramp. I put my head up to see where I was. There were low gleaming buildings and everywhere looked very clean.

Two ladies were standing near the ramp; when they saw me I heard one of them say: "Oh, isn't he beautiful!"

Will led me into a sparkling clean stable. It had a deep, clean wood shavings bed; even the bed seemed to sparkle. The stable did not look as if a horse had ever been in it before. Liz and Will went off with the two ladies and I explored my new stable. I was looking for anything that I could eat. At home I usually managed to find some bits of haylage on the ledge below the wire mesh, but this stable was so clean that I could not find anything to eat at all.

Very soon Liz came back with some haylage for me.

"Those two veterinary nurses think that you are beautiful Cayman! I'm very surprised; this is a hospital for racehorses *worth fortunes*, not for scruffy carthorses like you!"

I could tell that she was not *really* surprised though.

Liz stroked my neck and said very seriously:

"Cayman, you must be good. You're going to have an operation to make your foot better and, in about a week, I'll come and take you home."

She gave me a big kiss on my neck; I knew that she was sad as she left me.

I did have an operation on my right front foot, but I don't remember it because I was asleep. When Liz came back with Will to collect me, I was in a loose box with two veterinary nurses, one was grooming me and the other was stroking my face. A vet was changing the bandage on my foot. I heard Liz call out:

"Cayman!" I did not move. I was glad to see Liz, but I was not lonely or worried as so many people were being so kind to me all the time.

Liz and Will came into the loose box. Whilst Liz was talking to the vet, I nuzzled Will, he smelled of home:

"You're alright mate, you've been to a five star hotel and got very drunk, now it's time to go home." I was glad that Will had come to take me back.

On the journey home, I was not frightened. I knew what to expect, and when I arrived in the yard at Gunstone and went back into my own stable, with bits of haylage on the ledge below the wire mesh, I felt safe and happy to be home.

I was not allowed to go out into the field straight away. My foot had to heal up first, but after a while, I was allowed to go for short walks on the yard. The first time Liz tried to walk me, but I was not very well-behaved. I did not mean to be bad, but I had been inside for so long, that just walking in the yard and smelling the fresh air made me feel very excited. I wanted to jump about, and by mistake I barged into Liz a few times; she knew that I was not thinking about what I was doing at all. Liz decided that it would be safer if Will led me; he is used to handling stallions, who can behave like that all the time, so he stopped me behaving too dangerously.

When Liz did eventually let me out into the field, I knew that she was nervous; she led me down the lane in my bridle. Whenever I put my head up high, or tried to turn to look at things around me, she made the bit press my mouth, to get my head down or keep it straight. When we got to the gate, she unlatched it and then undid the nose band and throat lash of my bridle, before leading me into the field, turning me to face the gate and pulling my bridle over my ears, almost all in one movement. Before I knew what had happened, I was free for the first time in months. It was very early and I was the first horse in the field. I did not know what to do first: graze? buck? roll? gallop? I tried to do *everything*, all at once! Freedom felt *wonderful* – but very confusing.

When I had completely recovered Liz said that as I was five, it was time that we got down to some serious schooling and that we would have lessons with Helen, in the indoor school. Helen was very kind. When she first saw Liz riding me round the school, she told her:

"He's got nice conformation; his movements are big and

slow, so you must be careful not to push him out of his rhythm." Liz stroked my neck, she seemed pleased. Helen continued:

"Because of his Draught breeding, he won't be psychologically mature until he is about eight." Liz seemed surprised and sounded a bit disappointed:

"That's *ages*!"

In lessons Liz rode me for a while with some special reins, called a Market Harborough, to help me to learn how to carry myself. It was not long before I did not need the Market Harborough any more, because the muscles on the top of my neck and in my back end had developed so that I *was* carrying myself. We did a lot of walking and I tried my hardest to do what Liz asked. I enjoyed our lessons and always got praise from Liz and Helen at the end.

When we did jumping, it was really good fun. I did not always manage to jump well, but Helen was never cross with me, she said to Liz:

"He does not know where to put his six legs." I knew that Helen understood me, because when I was jumping it *did* feel as if I had lots of legs to control. Helen was also kind when I had problems cantering to the left. It was difficult to lead with the correct leg; to start with, if I was wrong, Helen asked Liz to stop me and set me off again. Eventually she let me keep going and sometimes I could sort out my legs, so that I got onto the correct leading leg, but it was tricky.

Liz and I went on lots of long hacks with Corris and Mrs B. I could tell that Liz was pleased with the way that I was growing up into a good riding horse. I knew that my mother would definitely be proud of me now. I felt fit and strong and I enjoyed being ridden by Liz.

My Second Operation at Newmarket

When I was seven, my left hock felt strange, it was a bit stiff. Liz noticed that, as I walked, the last part of the movement was jerky.

Jerry said that I had to have a picture taken of the bones in my hock. I went in the lorry with Sam and Liz to my other vet, Sue's yard. Jerry was there too. We were all in a shed and when the door was closed it was completely dark. There was a problem because my back leg was too big for the machine which took pictures of bones. Sue said:

"It's not designed for hairy yaks like him!"

A few days later, Liz told me that the picture of my hock showed that some extra bone was growing in my joint and that I would have to have *another* operation, to get rid of it. This time Sam and Will took me to Newmarket in the lorry. I was not frightened; I remembered how well I had been cared for last time.

After my hock operation, I had to stay in my stable for what seemed like forever. I almost forgot what 'outside' looked like. Liz did her best; she brought me interesting treats to eat, groomed me and sat in my stable to keep me company, but I still got *very* bored, I did not feel like putting my head up to look at anything, my whole body ached because I could not stretch properly; I was miserable. I often heard Liz asking Jerry to allow me out of my stable, but he said that I could not go out until my hock had recovered more. Liz was very worried that I was so unhappy.

Eventually, Jerry said that I could go into the indoor school to exercise myself and roll. When Liz led me out of my stable, my legs were so stiff that I had to concentrate very hard to make them walk at all. Liz was surprised when we got into the indoor school and I just stood still. She probably expected me to be frisky and buck and canter and roll, but it was so hard to walk that I did not feel frisky. Liz tried chasing me to get me moving, but I did not move much. After a few days of going into the indoor school, my legs started to come back to life and my body ached less, I felt a bit brighter too.

I was allowed to go for short walks round the yard in the morning and in the evening. Liz put on my bridle in case I was difficult to control, but there was nothing to get excited about in the yard. When Liz led me in the evenings, the air was damp and it was quite dark; the light on the garage nearly blinded us as we walked towards it, but when we walked away from it, the yard was dark. Usually everyone had gone home so it was quiet apart from the clatter of my hooves and the stomp of Liz's boots. If the dogs barked to start with, they quickly settled down to sleep again. There was just me and Liz walking round: past the house to the gateway, past the small wooden shed, past the telegraph pole, past the dog pen, past the garage and back to the house again. Sometimes we did it the other way round. My friend Skunk, who was sleek and shiny in the beam of light from the garage, would walk across the yard, pause in the middle and watch me for a moment. I could tell that he thought it was strange that I was being led round the yard in the dark, but as it was 'mouseing time', he had more important things to think about.

Liz tried to encourage me. She would look at the small shiny thing on her wrist a lot and say:

"Only another seven minutes Cayman, come on, cheer up, this is good for you, it will make your leg get better!" She stroked my neck as we walked round – and round – and round. Sometimes I think that I fell asleep as we walked, but when I woke up we would still be walking.

I could not believe it when one morning Liz came to my stable and said:

"Right Cayman, today we can go for a proper walk up the lane." I felt so excited as Liz led me out of the stable yard and up the hill that I could see out of my stable window. The lane is not very wide, with high hedges on both sides. I was wearing my bridle and Liz had her heavy boots and her riding hat and gloves on. I could tell that she was expecting trouble. Liz kept me walking straight up the hill, and then we turned into the farmyard on top of the hill. My head was high as I looked around the yard. We went down the track and soon we were between two hedges again. As Liz led me towards the gate on the track I was walking faster and faster. She made the bit press my mouth but it made no difference. I felt as if my energy was surging back. I think that Liz wanted me to stand at the gate, but as we approached, I could not stop myself pulling away from her and cantering back up the track. I was so excited that I did not know what I was doing. I caught sight of a gap in the hedge and dashed through it into the biggest field I had ever been in, it was sloping and the soil was so soft that my feet sank into it a long way. I galloped straight down to the bottom of the bank, along to the very end of the field by the road, and then back right across the field. The fresh air rolled into my lungs; I had so much energy that I felt as if every horse who had ever galloped, was galloping inside me. *Nothing* could have stopped me galloping.

I stopped in the top corner by the farmyard. I was so out of breath that I was dizzy and my legs were weak from the effort of pulling them out of the soft soil. I felt more full of life than I had done for as long as I could remember. As I stood trying to get my breath back, I could see Liz walking quickly up the track, she came into the field through another gap in the hedge. I put my head up high and watched her; she walked more slowly as she approached me. I knew that I had been very naughty to pull away from her and gallop off, but it was wonderful to really stretch my legs and feel the fresh air going into my nostrils.

Liz stretched out her arm and very quietly took hold of the rope attached to my bit. She probably thought that I was going to run off and gallop round the field again. I did not have the energy to do that even if I had wanted to, but I did not – once was enough.

Liz was not cross. She stood in front of me on my left side, looked up into my eye and stroked my jaw gently:

"It's alright Cayman, I understand why you galloped round the field, and you did look magnificent while you were doing it!"

Liz was worried that I might have damaged my leg, but as we walked back home she decided that it seemed alright.

When we got back into the yard, Will was there and Liz told him what I had done. She said that if the landowner contacted Will about enormous hoof prints across his spring corn, then she would have to admit that it was me. She said that as I was probably the only horse for miles around wearing huge egg-bar shoes, my hoof prints would be easy to identify.

It was not long before I was trotted-up for Jerry. At last, he told Liz that I could go out into my usual field again. He said that I was nine-tenths sound and that no one but a dressage judge would notice that I was not completely sound. *I* knew that I was better because of my gallop, but I do not think that Liz told Jerry about that.

The corn must have grown quickly and covered my hoof prints because no one contacted Will about them, so we did not get into trouble. The hair grew back on my left hind leg and the next time Jerry saw me, he told Liz that I had become "elegant". Liz was really pleased; she told me that – although, as I was growing up, I sometimes looked like a big old grey donkey, whose feet and head were too big – she had always known that eventually I would turn into a beautiful elegant horse – and that now I had. I felt happy that Liz was proud of me.

'People always noticed my feet'

Chapter Seven

CORRIS

*C*orris told me that he was so superior in every way, that it was an honour for me to go for rides with him, have a stable next to his and graze with him; most of the time Corris ignored me. Corris is Liz's mother Mrs B.'s horse, he is 15hh, his father was a Fell pony and his mother was Thoroughbred, Corris has perfect conformation. He was dappled grey with a black mane and tail but now he is white.

Mrs B. said that she had been Corris's person since he was six and that he was born in Dolgellau in north Wales, then he lived in Borth in mid Wales, then he came to our stables at Gunstone Hall. She said that before she became his person, Corris's name had been Prince William, because he was born in the same year as Prince William, and that she had changed his name to Corris, which is a place near to Dolgellau. *Corris said* that before he came to Gunstone Hall, his name had been Prince William because he was owned by the Queen, and he was her favourite horse...

Accomplishments

When I was three, Corris was fifteen; he had already done *everything* that a horse could do. He said that in Borth he had been a trekking horse, but that he had never had to do any work because he learned that if he threw his head up and snatched the reins out of his rider's hands, they could not control him, so he could do whatever he wanted.

Corris said that he came to Gunstone Hall when it was a riding school and for eight years people learned to ride on him. In fact, he said, he was the cleverest horse in the school, so everyone wanted to ride him. He was *so clever* that when the instructor taught all the horses something new, he would instantly work out an evasion, so she taught Corris his own, more difficult version of everything, to keep him entertained.

Turn on the forehand, to canter, was easy for Corris.

I heard Mrs B. say that if Corris could not be bothered to try in a lesson, he would switch his brain off and act like a dead donkey. If the instructor got on him, he would buck all round the school, but when he was used in a lesson for people with disabilities, he behaved perfectly and took extra special care of his rider.

Corris was so famous that wherever Mrs B. went *without* him, people would ask her if she had a horse called 'Corris', and wherever she went *with* him, people would ask:

"Is that Corris?" She said that he taught half the county to ride.

Will was a professional showjumper; he heard that Corris could jump, so Corris and Will went showjumping. Will said that Corris's only problem was that because he loved jumping, he jumped so unnecessarily big, that he spent far too long soaring through the air. But Corris was not daunted, he became even more legendary when he did cross country. He was going too fast to stop when the horse in front of him jumped and then *did stop*, on the landing side of the jump. As Corris's way over the jump was blocked, he jumped the fence at the side of it, at an angle. Will said that that fence was 4ft 6ins!

With Mrs B. Corris did some dressage, but what he really enjoyed was endurance riding. He regularly did twenty-mile rides and became so fit that he and Mrs B. qualified for the British Horse Society's Bronze Buckle.

Once, when Mrs B. intended to take Corris on a 'fun ride' at Weston Park, *Corris* decided that he did not want to go into the trailer. So, Mrs B. rode him to Weston (twelve miles), did the fun ride (five miles), and rode him home again (twelve miles). Corris trotted most of the way home!

'The Perfect Pony'

Our teacher Helen told Liz that, as I was a Draught horse, I would not be grown-up until I was eight. I could not wait to be eight, I hoped that then, I would be as clever as Corris. When I *was* eight, I was very disappointed when Liz said:

"Oh dear Cayman, is this all we are going to get?"

If Liz really needed a clever horse, she used Corris. Once, Liz needed to practise lungeing for her exam. When I was very young I was quite good at lungeing, but it had been a few years since I had done any and I had forgotten what to do. We were in the indoor school, rays of sunlight were coming in through the wooden slats at the top of the wall, they were getting in my eyes and making it hard for me to see. I could not understand why Liz was making me go away from her, she was stern and had a big whip in her hand. Usually she wanted me to come to her, but now she was sending me away. Didn't she like me any more? I did not know what to do, so I stood still and pawed the ground with all my effort, right from my shoulder. I was so confused. That seemed to have a magical effect on Liz, she was laughing kindly as she walked towards me; she quickly unclipped the side-reins from my bit, then stood in front of me and rubbed my forehead:

"Oh Cayman, you look like a magnificent Lipizzaner stallion! If it upsets you so much, we don't have to bother with lungeing." I was glad.

Liz did practise lungeing with Corris though, and I heard her say that he went round as if he was on a merry-go-round, in walk, trot and canter; and that he could even do direct transitions: from halt to trot, or trot to halt, on the lunge. She called him 'Little Goody Two Shoes'. I felt jealous because Liz was *my* person.

It got worse! For her exam Liz also had to practise jumping. I did not learn to jump well until I went to school at Rodbaston Agricultural College when I was ten, so Liz had to practise on Corris. Liz did not normally ride him, so she explained, to anyone who asked why she was riding him, that:

"Corris is *brilliant* at jumping!" After he had jumped, Corris was all puffed-up with even more self-importance than usual. He boasted that Liz called him 'The Perfect Pony', although he said that he was "actually a horse".

Electric Fences

Corris even understood electric fences, which most of us were frightened of.

The field by the lake, where Sam's horses live, had been divided into four paddocks by electric fencing. The paddocks went down the field, one leading into the next. Liz had to get Corris in from the fourth paddock, right at the bottom. The next day I heard Liz tell Mrs B. that she had been amazed by Corris:

"I could not see how to get him out of the bottom paddock, because I could not see where to unhook the fence. I was leading him along the fence, looking for the way out, when he very rudely snatched away. He walked along the fence and then stood facing it. When I got there, I could see that he was facing the part of the fence that could be unhooked, to allow us into the next paddock. When we came to the second fence, Corris led me straight to the right place to get through that fence, even though the way out was in a different place from the first fence. By the time we got to the third fence, I just left it to Corris to find the way out. The third way out was in a different place in the fence from either of the other two, but Corris found it with no problem!"

I could tell by her voice that Liz was in awe of Corris, just like everyone else. She was even more amazed when Mrs B. told her that Corris had not been put into the bottom paddock through the other paddocks, but that, on the day when she got him in, and on the previous day, he had jumped in, over the cross country jump, from the geldings' field. So when he had shown Liz the way out of the paddocks, he had only been that way *once* before.

My experience of electric fences was a bit different. When I was about eight, I was standing by the stream with Liz, when she pointed to the thin fence which made a clicking sound and said:

"That is an electric fence Cayman, you must *not* touch it." Usually when Liz pointed at something it meant that she wanted me to investigate it, so I stretched out my nose close to the fence. My whiskers only just touched it, when the fence gave me the biggest bite on my nose that I had ever had. It all happened so quickly, I was very surprised. I did not know how the fence could have bitten me – it was confusing. I thought that maybe Liz had made the fence bite me, but she did not usually do things like that. As the pain of the bite sank into my nose – which is very sensitive – I could not stop myself turning and galloping, as fast as I could, right across the field, as far away from the fence as possible. I made sure that I always stayed away from it; it had bitten me without even moving, I could not trust it.

Trying to be Friendly

My stable was next to Corris's and sometimes I would stretch my neck out, over my top rail, to try to talk to him. I was only trying to be friendly, but Corris would lunge at me with his ears back and his teeth barred. I did not know why Corris was so unfriendly, so I would try again – and each time he tried to bite me. Liz was afraid that I would bang my head on the wall dividing our stables, as I had to pull away from Corris very quickly. She was so concerned that a special 'weaving gate' had to be put up, to stop me stretching over my top rail. Liz told me that it was for my own protection because it would stop Corris attacking me.

When Corris and I went to school at Rodbaston Agricultural College, we were put in stables next to each other because the people there knew that we were 'stable mates'. Although we grazed in the same field, Corris was so horrible to me in the stable, that we had to be separated; he was sent to a stable out of sight, in a different part of the yard. I think that the people at Rodbaston knew about Corris though, because Liz said that when I went to school she had to say what I was like, and that was written on my stable door, to help the students to handle me. Mrs B. would have done the same.

On my stable door it said:

Cayman 17hh
10yr old Gelding
TB x Draught
Docile Very willing
Hack

On Corris's stable door it said:

Corris 15hh
22yr old Gelding
Fell x TB
Good to handle *Opinionated*
Dressage Jump XC Endurance Hack

Being Kept Waiting

Sometimes Mrs B. looked after both me and Corris. We were very fortunate, Mrs B. is a very kind person, she looked after us so well. Mrs B. is more reliable than Liz. Liz would sometimes keep us waiting in the field, when it was time to go into our stables. When this happened I did not mind, I just ate more grass and waited because I knew that Liz would come eventually; but Corris got very annoyed, he said that Mrs B never kept him waiting. Corris was very fond of Mrs B. He did not even *try* to be friendly with other people or horses. He was not like me, I could not help being friendly with everyone. I wanted everyone to be friendly with me, but Corris ignored everyone except Mrs B. and sometimes, when he thought he knew best, he even ignored her too.

Black Snakes

When we did 'Flying Horses', which is quite a long ride, Corris refused to go through the strawberry field because he said that it was full of black snakes, and Mrs B., Liz and I must be stupid if we thought that it was safe. Mrs B. told Corris that there were no snakes, only black pipes to water the strawberries, but no one, not even Mrs B. could make Corris walk through the field.

I trusted Liz and walked right through the middle, with the black pipes all around my feet, because that was what Liz wanted me to do. Corris cantered round the edge of the strawberry field, on the stubble. When we met at the gate, he insisted that the only reason that the black snakes had not attacked me was because they had already eaten enough strawberries, so they were not hungry. I did not argue with Corris.

Pinky

Corris said that before our field was 'the geldings' field', mares used to be in it too, and that he had a girlfriend called Pinky. She was white like him, and they grazed together. He said that he lost interest in Pinky when he found out that she was not clever enough to get out into the next field with him, by jumping the cross country jump. As the grass in the next field was far better he soon forgot about Pinky, because there was no point in having a girlfriend who was not nearly as clever as he was.

The Boss

In the geldings' field Corris was the dominant gelding. If a new horse came into the field, Corris would quietly walk up to him and warn him that *he* was the boss and that so long as the new horse did not upset him, and showed him respect, then things would be alright. Sometimes, if a new horse was young, he might try to challenge Corris; he would only make that mistake once. Some horses had the teeth marks on their necks or shoulders to remind them that Corris was the boss. He made me graze with him. Sometimes, especially when I was young, I wanted to play with the other horses, but I did not dare disobey Corris.

One day I was playing by the gate with Sooty and quite a few of the other youngsters, we were all having fun. Corris had been out for a ride and when Mrs B. turned him into the field, the other horses parted respectfully, to allow him to walk through the middle of them. I was having such a good game with Sooty, that I did not notice that Corris had come back into the field. He walked a little way from the gateway and then stopped. All of the other horses, including the youngsters, were standing, but Sooty and I were still playing 'biting and chasing'. Suddenly, I realized that we were the only ones who were playing. I could feel Corris looking hard at me, I felt very uncomfortable. I knew that I could not finish my game with Sooty. I had no choice, I had to walk behind Corris to wherever he wanted to graze.

When it was time for us to come in, Corris insisted on being brought in first. If Mrs B. arrived to get him in before Liz came to get me in, that was fine, Corris was happy. Sometimes, but not very often, Liz would arrive first; that would make Corris furious. He would come to the gate with me and then, although we had been grazing together all day, he would run at me with his teeth barred and his ears back, or he would turn round and buck at me, but not kick out his back legs. Liz just told him to "Go away!" and he would walk crossly, up to the stile at the top of the field, to wait for Mrs B.

It was not just me that Corris threatened by the gate, it was any horse that happened to be there. The worst thing was that if I grazed with Corris, he expected me to be aggressive like him. He had forgotten that he made me graze with him. So that Corris would think that I was aggressive, I always bit Harley if he was in the gateway. Harley never bit anyone back, so I was quite safe.

Being in the gateway could get really dangerous, when either Liz or Mrs B. was bringing us both in. As Corris thought that he should always go in first, he sometimes made such a fuss that Liz did get him in first. Then, it was my turn to walk up to the stile and wait. I was not cross, but I did feel left-out because Liz was *my* person. Corris never let Mrs B. take me in first.

Liz said that I would never be as clever as Corris. I was glad about that, I was happy as I was; Corris was *too* clever.

Corris, aged 24, being impatient to get going on a fun ride.

Chapter Eight

FOOD

*F*ood is the most important thing. We eat most of the time, grass is our favourite. When we are not eating, we are usually *thinking* about eating.

People often give us interesting food from bags that rustle. When you see a person eating some food, or hear a person rustle a bag, you can ask them to share the food, by pointing your ears as far forward as they will go and looking at the food, or the bag, with your eyes very wide; this usually works. People seem to like sharing their food with us. Sometimes, if they do not know you, they can't believe how quickly you can eat, so they give you more, to prove how quickly you ate what they gave you first. Then, they give you even more to see whether you can carry on eating so fast. They look a bit surprised when all of their food has gone. If the person knows you though, it is different...

Apples and Carrots

When Liz first became my person, she was very strict; she said that she must teach me to be polite. When she offered me a carrot or an apple, she would hold it very tightly, so that I could not eat it all at once. Liz taught me to take bites and she did not let me take another bite until the first one was chewed up and swallowed. To start with I worried that the carrot or the apple would go away whilst I did this, but it never did; it could not because Liz was holding it. I did not have to worry that another horse would get it because Liz was my person and she said that it was for me. Liz was proud of me for being so polite.

Our teacher Helen taught Liz 'bendy carrots'. 'Bendy carrots' was to help me to flex my neck after I had been schooled. Liz would stand behind my front leg on my left side, with a big carrot. To eat the carrot I had to stretch my neck round and take one bite. Next we did the same on my right side, and then still standing behind my front legs, Liz held the last piece of carrot between my front legs so that I had to stretch my neck down until my mouth reached my chest.

Liz and I both got the hang of 'bendy carrots', so I decided that if I wanted to tell Liz that I *wanted* a carrot, I could, by bobbing my head round to my left, round to my right, then under my chest. As Liz was good at her part of 'bendy carrots' she would understand and I would get a carrot. I thought that my idea was very clever.

The first time that I asked Liz for a carrot like this, I was very pleased when she said:

"Oh Cayman, you're so clever – you're doing 'bendy carrots'!" I thought that she would give me a carrot, but I was disappointed when she said:

"I haven't got any carrots – anyway you needn't think that every time you do that, I'm going to give you a carrot!" Liz stroked me, that was nice – but I really *did* want a carrot.

Cow Parsley

When we went out for rides, when I was very young, I was never allowed to eat. Liz probably knew that if she had allowed me to eat whilst I was being ridden, we would not have got further than the grass verge just after the gate across the lane, which goes up the hill behind my stable. That is where the best grazing is, especially in summer. As well as long sweet grass, there is every sort of plant you could think of, and they are all in one place, so you can enjoy lots of lovely tastes without having to search for them. When I was older, Liz did allow me to eat when we were out, but only when she said I could. I did not mind, it was a treat, and it was certainly better than not ever being allowed to eat on rides. Liz knew how much I loved cow parsley; she said that as it was good for me, I could eat it as we walked by the grass verges where it grew. It was convenient that it grew to just the same height as my mouth.

Corris loved cow parsley too; he was so expert at snipping it off with his front teeth, that no one noticed him snatching it as he went past. I only knew that he had got some cow parsley because I could see his mouth moving as he chewed it. I was not as good as Corris at snipping off cow parsley. Sometimes, as I grabbed at a big stalk while walking, I did not manage to snip it off and as my teeth were still clamped onto it, it would bring me to an abrupt halt. Or, if the stalk was in light, sandy soil, the whole plant would be uprooted, so that I walked along with the top in my mouth and the rest, right down to the roots and soil, dragging between my front legs. If I did manage to snip off cow parsley properly, but there was too much to fit in my mouth, Corris would often steal the bit that was dangling. Whatever happened, Liz would laugh at me, she obviously did not know how difficult it was to snip off cow parsley with your front teeth and walk at the same time.

Thistles

Liz also knew that I loved thistle flowers, we did not see them very often and sometimes Liz would notice them first; she always let me eat them. Eating thistle flowers is *very* tricky, you have to be careful that the sharp spikes under the flower do not stick into your lips, because that is painful and the spikes stay in your lips for a long time. If I was eating a thistle flower whilst I was wearing my bridle, so my bit was in my mouth, Liz would help me by not moving the reins at all, so that the bit stayed completely still, whilst I very delicately plucked the flower off with my front teeth. Liz understood that I had to do this carefully, so that my lips did not get spikes in them.

Damsons

In autumn Liz and I could eat damsons. One of the best places to do this was at the end of the lane near the church at Bishops Wood. From my back, Liz could reach as many damsons as she wanted. I could not understand why she ate damsons the way she did though. Liz just ate the fruit and spat out the stones, that was really wasteful. The way that I eat damsons is much better; I bite off a whole branch, that way I can eat everything: leaves, wood, fruit, stones. Liz would never fill herself up the way she eats damsons.

Liz's way of eating damsons is also dangerous. We were trotting along the Kiddemore Green Road when Liz made a spitting noise and something suddenly darted down my left shoulder. Instinctively I jumped sideways into the middle of the road, fortunately there were no cars coming. How was I to know that it was only a damson stone? I do not know why Liz did not chew it up properly.

Chocolate Biscuits

Once, when it was Christmas, Harley's person Claire gave him chocolate biscuits. Claire said that Liz could give me some (Harley did not know). Chocolate biscuits are really for people; they are in stuff that rustles. Liz stood in front of my stable, and I could see that she was fiddling with something. As soon as I heard rustling I was very excited, I thought that it might have something to do with food. I pointed both ears to what Liz was fiddling with and flared my nostrils to try to smell what it was. Liz seemed to take so long to do everything to do with food, I was getting exasperated.

At last, Liz pulled out something flat and round, and put it on the palm of her hand. She held her hand under my muzzle and instantly the thing was in my mouth; but as I bit it, it changed from being hard – to being like sand. I was surprised. Nothing that I had ever eaten before had done that, and it did not feel right. Unlike dogs and cats, we cannot be sick, we are easily poisoned if we eat something that we should not eat. We are very good at spitting things out; so that is what I did. The strange stuff flew out of my mouth as I threw my head up and down as quickly as I could, whilst I used my tongue to make sure that it had all gone.

As I spat out the last bits, I wondered why Liz was trying to poison me, and why she seemed to think that it was funny! I was surprised when Liz got out another flat round thing, put it on the palm of her hand; and held it under my muzzle:

"Cayman, I am not trying to poison you, this is a chocolate biscuit and it is nice!" She sounded so sure about the last part, that I opened my mouth a bit and let her push the chocolate biscuit in. Once it was in, she held her hand flat under my muzzle and kept it there, so that it was difficult for me to open my mouth again. When I chewed the biscuit it turned into sand, just like the first one had done. As it did so, Liz said in her 'very encouraging voice', that she used when I did not want to do something:

"Mmmmm, yummy, scrummy, biscuit." As she said that, the biscuit started to taste sweet, but before I knew what had happened, and because it was not very big, I had swallowed it.

Liz then turned to Corris who was in the next stable. Corris had left his haylage to see what Liz was giving me, and if it was food, to see whether he could have some too. It was alright for me to have some of Harley's chocolate biscuits, but I was very surprised when Liz gave one of them to Corris. Corris ate it as if he had chocolate biscuits every day. I could tell that he liked it. I decided that I could not let *my* person feed *my* chocolate biscuits to Corris, so I pressed my chest against my top rail and stuck my nose out as far as I could towards the biscuits which Liz was holding. My eyes were very wide and my ears were very far forward, Liz always knew what that meant. It worked. Liz turned back to me, she was laughing at me again:

"So you like them after all do you? Or is it just because I'm giving them to Corris?"

The third chocolate biscuit that Liz gave me was the sweetest thing I have tasted since the farmer put sticky stuff on my bit when I first wore a bridle. It was lovely! I wanted more biscuits, lots of them, and quickly! I know that Liz knew what I wanted, but she said:

"You can't have any more Cayman, three is enough, they are not good for your teeth."

I was amazed that Liz could be so unfair. She had encouraged me to eat chocolate biscuits and just when I decided that they were the best thing I had ever tasted, she was not going to let me have any more. I could not believe that she had mentioned teeth, when people ate chocolate biscuits and their teeth were too weak even to eat damson stones. I did get more chocolate biscuits though. The next Christmas, for a special treat, Liz got some just for me, but she never let me have more than three a day.

Wormer

There was one thing that we had to eat, that none of us liked, that was wormer. We always knew when it was worming time, because the first horse to be wormed in our stable block would tell his or her neighbour, who would pass it on, so we all quickly found out and started to feel unsettled. I was usually one of the last to be wormed. I had to have one and a third syringes of wormer; to get the third, I shared with George and Rupert who are the same size as me. Some horses got so upset that Sam or Will, or even both Sam *and* Will, had to give them their wormer, because their people could not do it. My wormer was always left by my stable for Liz to give me. It tasted so horrible that most of us tried to spit it out straight away but that did not work because it stuck to our tongues. If our people held our heads up by putting their hands under our jaws, and massaged our throats, we usually had to swallow the wormer, which was what they wanted us to do. Sometimes we had wormer which Liz said was 'apple flavoured'- if apples tasted as bad as that wormer, we would never eat them.

I tried to hide from Liz when I knew that she was going to give me wormer. I stood with my head in one of the corners of my stable furthest from the doorway. I kept my head low and hoped that she would not notice me. As usual Liz laughed at me. She would scratch the top of my tail and tell me that when my stable was only a few feet longer than I was, it was impossible for me to hide in it. Having my tail scratched made me feel a bit less anxious about the horrible taste which I knew would soon be in my mouth, so I would turn round. Sometimes Liz would put on my head collar, but not always. She stood by my head and rubbed the syringe of wormer gently against the side of my mouth. I clamped my lips shut and put my head up as high as I could. After a while my neck ached, so I would drop my head a bit lower. Having the syringe rubbed against the side of my mouth made me think of food and when I did that, I would forget to keep my lips clamped shut. Liz was very clever at worming because as soon as my head was down and my lips were not clamped shut, she would push the syringe into the corner of my mouth and squirt the wormer onto the back of my tongue. This made my head shoot up again, but it was too late, I had had one syringe of wormer. The last third of a syringe was easy for Liz to give me because I was so upset by the first one that I could not concentrate on resisting the second one. After she had given me the wormer, Liz always rubbed my forehead a lot and told me how good I had been; she gave me a carrot and then my feed. I could not taste the carrot because of the taste of the wormer, but by the time I was half way through my feed, it tasted like it usually did.

Corris got so angry with Mrs B. when she gave him wormer, that he managed to walk round his stable, with his back end to her all the time. He flatly refused to make friends with her by eating a carrot that she offered and was not keen to eat his feed. But by the next morning Corris was always friendly again with Mrs B.

Although wormer tasted horrible, our people were not trying to be cruel. Liz told me that if I had worms, they would live inside me and eat all my food, so I would become ill. I certainly did not like the sound of anything eating my food, so I thought that probably our people *were* doing what was best for us.

Hurry Up!

When people give you your feed, they always do it so slowly. At Gunstone, there are a lot of people – at least one per horse. That meant that at evening feed time a lot of them would be there together. I do not think that people live in herds like we do, but it seemed as if they wanted to, because when they were supposed to be getting our feeds, they would stand in groups and talk. It was really frustrating for us – didn't they know that we wanted our feeds?

Some horses were very patient and just stood looking over their rails, waiting. Others ate haylage whilst they waited. I hated waiting for my feed, but I discovered a trick to make it come faster. I would whirl round once in my stable and then stand at the doorway. If that did not work, I would whirl round twice and then stand at the doorway. Liz never ignored me, she said that I looked magnificent when I did this. She was so proud of me that she would stop talking and give me my feed. My trick always worked.

'Grass is our favourite'

Chapter Nine

GOOD MANNERS

*A*s my mother was a docile Draught horse, whose ancestors worked alongside people for hundreds of years, pulling loads and ploughing fields, Liz said that I would have been born with good manners; but that as I weighed three-quarters of a ton, it would be safer if she taught me even more good manners, to go with the ones that I already had. So, right from when she became my person when I was three, Liz taught me good manners and made sure that I always used them.

Liz used good manners too, when she was handling me she was kind and considerate. I usually knew how she would behave and she usually knew how I would behave, so we could trust each other, and enjoy being together.

I'll tell you about my manners, which were *nearly* always good ...

Traffic

Liz told me that, for the sake of my own safety and hers, good manners in traffic were most important. To start to teach me about traffic when I was very young, Liz took me to Brewood. Brewood is a village with a square in the middle; cars and people come and go all day long. We went one afternoon when Liz said that it would not be too busy. So that I could get used to traffic, Liz wanted me to stand in the square where I could see the traffic coming and going. At the top of the square is a big shop, a lot of cars were parked along the road outside the shop, but there was one space left. As I was nearly as long as a car, Liz decided that we could stand in the space, where we would be out of the way. I did not mind; as Liz 'parked' me alongside the pavement, between the cars, I felt quite safe. It is about three miles from Gunstone to Brewood, and I did feel a bit tired.

A few cars drove past, a few more approached from straight ahead and then turned either left or right and went away. I had forgotten that we were in Brewood to learn about traffic and that I was supposed to watch what was going on. I rested a back leg, hung my head, closed my eyes, and let my bottom lip flop. My snooze did not last long though, I heard Liz laughing; she stroked my neck:

"Cayman you're supposed to be watching and learning. I suppose you can't help taking after your carthorse ancestors, I can just imagine you parked up, the cart with its brake on, and a nose bag full of carrots." I liked the sound of 'a nose bag full of carrots' and thought that if that was what carthorses got, I would not mind being one, like my ancestors. Liz could tell that I had good manners in traffic, so we went home.

My manners were so good that as I got older, Liz took me on roads with far more traffic than in the square in Brewood. She said that some horses were frightened in traffic because some cars went past them too close and too fast. In the summer when I was twelve, Liz started riding me down the Brewood Road between Brewood and Gunstone. Cars go very fast on that road. She said that as I was so well-mannered in traffic, she had a duty to ride me there, to remind car drivers that horses also use roads. Because I was 17hh and nearly white, Liz said that drivers would notice me – and might even think that I was a police horse. She said that if we reminded drivers about horses, that might make the road safer for other horses and riders.

I enjoyed walking down the Brewood Road, it made a change to go that way, and the summer was so hot that I was happy to walk steadily. The traffic never frightened me – and I know that Liz felt safe on my back.

Being Caught

When Liz came into my field, she did not march straight up to me and put on my head collar. I would not have minded if she had, but she said that she knew that horses found that sort of behaviour from humans threatening. Instead, if Liz wanted to come to me in the field, she would walk up to me slowly, with her eyes down, rather than looking hard, straight at me. She would speak softly to me as she approached, then she would stand a short distance from me, which made me want to go to her.

When I was grown up, Liz always greeted me in my field by kissing the left side of my nose, she said it was velvety and smelled nice: I did not mind. Then she would say:

"Hello Cayman, what have you been doing today?" Liz always knew what I had been doing, because she would answer:

"Eating grass and playing with your silly friends I expect."

If I had mud on the side of my face, in my mane and on my withers and rump, she would know that I had been rolling, or if it was a hot day and I had mud on all of my legs half-way up to my knees, she knew that I had been standing in the stream to keep cool.

There was not much that Liz did not know about. She told me that if I was ever naughty when she was not there, she would find out because one of the other people would tell her. I could tell that she did not really think that I was going to be naughty.

Sometimes in summer, Liz would surprise me by appearing at the Brewood Road end of my field, not at the gateway as usual. If I was waiting by the gate, I would turn round and look to see that it really was Liz, then I would set off across the field to greet her, even though that meant that we would then both have to walk back to the gate.

When I was twelve, Liz acted very strangely. Rather than walking slowly up to me, with her eyes down as usual, Liz started to run straight towards me, with her arms stretched out on each side. At that speed she had to look straight at me, otherwise she might have fallen over, it is difficult to run on only two legs. I just kept on walking towards Liz – at least I had good manners. Liz must have noticed how surprised I looked. When she got up to me, she put her arms round my neck and said:

" Hello Boo Boo, I was just testing you!" I do not know what happened to *her* manners that day...

Liz would sometimes do what she called 'Monty Roberts catching'. She told me that she had asked Monty Roberts how she could avoid having to walk right across my field in the summer, when I could not be bothered to walk to her because I really just wanted to carry on eating grass. After Monty Roberts told her what to do, Liz would walk into the field, stand and look hard at my side – just in front of my back legs – for a while, before turning and walking away. If I was in the wild I would be an animal that got eaten. I can tell when I am being looked at, because it might be a predator looking at me, getting ready to leap, and sink its claws and teeth into me. So, Liz could get my attention that way. I would lift my head up from the grass and see that it was Liz, not a predator, looking at me. But then, as I am a herd animal and Liz is my herd leader, I want to be with her, so when she walks away I want to follow her.

'Monty Roberts catching' worked so well that if Liz started to run away from me, I would become anxious and break into a trot, or even a canter, to catch up with her. Monty Roberts saved Liz from sometimes having to walk a long way across my field, which was very big.

Stable Manners

Liz told me that the place where good manners were most important was in my stable. I just about filled my stable, so when there was a person in it too, I had to be very careful not to tread on their feet, or squash them against the wall.

Liz approached me in my stable in the same way as she approached me in my field. If I had not seen her come into the stable block because I was snoozing, or looking out of the window at the lane that goes up the hill, she would speak softly to me as she approached my stable, so that I was not startled.

If I had just woken up from a snooze I would often stretch my back and neck; I did this by stretching out both front legs and arching my neck, whilst I pulled my whole body back so that my rump stayed high up on my straight back legs, whilst my shoulders went down very low, so that my withers were only up to Liz's waist – normally they were up to the top of her head. Liz always stayed outside my stable whilst I stretched, there was not room for her to come in; she said that dogs stretched like I did.

Stretching my back legs in the stable was a problem, they were too long, so my hoof usually hit the wall before my leg was stretched out as far as it would go. Liz could stretch my front legs for me, by firmly holding one leg out in front of me with both hands and telling me to "S-T-R-E-E-T-C-H", whilst I pulled my body away from it.

I always had to have my feet picked out before I left my stable, so that the wood shavings that were stuck in them did not fall out on the path and make a mess. When Mrs B. looked after me and Corris, she taught us a useful trick. Rather than risking getting squashed by going behind me in the stable, she taught me to have all four hooves picked out from the left side, this was very easy for us both. Mrs B reached under my belly, ran her hand down my leg from my knee, or at the back, my hock, and said:

"Up foot!" In no time, I had learned to lift my right front leg so that she could pull it across behind my left front leg, and then to lift my right back leg and bring it across in front of my left back leg. All four hooves got picked out very quickly that way.

I was so good at this that I could even do it in the field, but there I did it an even easier way. Liz or Mrs B. still stayed on my left side and when they touched a leg, I just bent my knee or hock a bit and let my hoof roll forward and balance on its toe, that way Liz or Mrs B. could see inside my hoof without even having to lift it up. They did this to make sure that there was nothing stuck in my hoof which could hurt me; there was not usually anything that needed picking out. I could have my hooves checked like this without even lifting my head off the grass, so no eating time was lost.

Before Mrs B. started turning Corris and me out in the mornings, Liz used to turn me out very early, before most of the other horses. I did not really like this, it was too early and often I had not finished snoozing.

One morning, Liz was picking out my hooves as usual, but when she lifted up my left hind leg, it did not feel as if it had woken up properly and a sharp pain shot through it. My leg kicked out very hard all by itself. As Liz had been holding my leg, she seemed to go with it – and ended up flat on my straw bed. As she stood up and started to rub her leg, she looked really angry. I was alarmed because I had never seen Liz looking like that before. She looked *very* threatening, so I tried to flatten myself against the back wall of my stable. Liz stood facing me, looking hard at me, then she roared:

" If you're going to kick me, I'll kick you!"

I was confused. Liz had never roared at me before, I did not like it. I stood frozen, pressed along the wall and did not know what to do. Liz stepped back, rubbing her leg as she did so and then leaned against the opposite wall; she was still looking at me hard. I felt frightened, Liz was my person, I relied on her to look after me and now that I had kicked her, she probably would not want to look after me anymore. I would be all alone. Being alone was frightening. I was very sorry for hurting Liz; I did not mean to kick her, my leg just shot out by itself. I had to let Liz know how sorry I was, and that I did not want to be alone.

I put my head down, lower than my withers, and slowly walked up to Liz. I put my forehead against her chest, and stayed there. I was so relieved when I felt Liz stroke my neck gently and firmly:

"Oh Cayman, you're saying you're sorry aren't you?" she said. I was glad that Liz understood, and that she was still my person and I would not be alone after all.

In the winter, when I had breakfast before I went out, Liz could muck-out round me. It was quite easy. Whilst I was eating, Liz would do one side of the stable, then she would say: "Over!" and I would move sideways, still with my nose in my breakfast bucket, so that she could do the other side. That way, by the time I had finished my breakfast, everything had been done. Liz said that she would not want to muck-out round most horses, because most horses did not have good manners like me.

Grooming

As I got older, my belly got more and more ticklish. Until I was about nine, I could be groomed all over with no problem, but then my belly changed. When Liz tried to brush mud off my belly, it felt so ticklish that I had to make her stop. I did this by bringing my back leg forwards under my belly, so that it nearly reached my front legs and then pushing it out sideways, so that it scooped Liz away. To start with Liz thought that I was just being bad mannered and firmly told me:

"I'm not having you cow-kicking Cayman, just behave!" Although my belly still tickled, I tried hard not to scoop Liz out of the way, but it was so difficult that it made me feel cross.

It was not until I went to live at Rodbaston Agricultural College, when I was ten and Liz's friend Gill saw the problem that Liz was having when she groomed my belly, that Gill said:

"He must be ticklish." After that, Liz always rubbed mud off my belly with her hand, which felt firmer, so it did not tickle me. I was really glad that Gill knew what was wrong with me, because when I had tried to tell Liz, in the only way I could think of, she thought that I had forgotten about good manners.

When Liz groomed me, it could take a long time. That was not because she did so much grooming, it was because we kept doing other things, like 'Eyes'. 'Eyes' is a sort of game, it makes you feel very sleepy.

I did not like having my face groomed with a brush

because it felt too scratchy, so Liz would rub mud off my face with her hand. To start with, I did not like that either. I tried to put my head up out of her reach, but Liz had long arms. Once she began to rub my face, I felt more relaxed and would lower my head. Liz stood at the side of my head and when my eye was level with her eyes, she would put her face to mine, so that one of her eyes was looking right into my eye. That always made me want to close both of my eyes. I felt very sleepy. Liz would stay there, with her eye to my eye, until something disturbed us, or we had to wake up because Mrs B. had finished grooming Corris and they were ready to go for a ride.

Liz also did something else which could take up a lot of time: I did not like having my forelock groomed, so again, I put my head right up to stop Liz reaching it, but she would stand close to me and stroke the top of my neck, which made me want to bring my head down. When it was low enough, Liz would slip her arm over my neck, a little way behind my ears. That made me feel very safe. It reminded me of when I was a foal and I used to hide under my mother's belly. I felt so safe close to Liz, with her arm over my neck, that I would drop my head right down so that she could brush my forelock from where it started, on the very top of my head between my ears. Even if my forelock did not need any more grooming, I would stay under Liz's arm, feeling safe and sleepy, until something made a noise, which woke me up. Liz and I were never ready to go for a ride before Mrs B. and Corris.

Leah

Sometimes Leah would help to groom me. Leah was a little girl who was four; she did not even come up to the top of my front legs. Leah's elder sister Laura, and her mother and father were all Sooty's people. Leah was too, but when we were in our stables Leah spent more time stroking me than Sooty. Leah's father called me a 'gentle giant'.

Leah was so small that when my weaving gate was not across the doorway to my stable, and I could put my head over the top rail, her father said that I looked like a dinosaur as I stretched my neck right down so that my eyes were level with Leah's eyes and we could talk to each other.

If my weaving gate was across the doorway, I had to thread my head between the top rail and the top of the wooden board, so that I could talk to Leah. Leah was the smallest person I had ever seen; she was my friend.

Leah spent ages arranging my forelock; her little hands felt like moths fluttering against my forehead, which made me sleepy. When Liz arrived, Leah would tell her:

" I've helped you groom Cayman!" Once, when I could feel that Leah had divided my forelock down the middle and pushed part to one side and part to the other side, so that my forehead felt bare, I heard her say to Liz:

"He must not have his mane in his eyes." Leah's own forelock was neatly divided so that it was not in her eyes either.

In the evenings Leah helped Liz to get my feed ready. Leah was so small that Liz would often not know that she was there, but Leah would pop up from behind a feed bin and say to Liz:

"Here I am! Can I help you make Cayman's tea?"

Liz always let Leah help her. Liz put a scoop of 'Alfa' and a scoop of 'Mix' in my big flat bucket, then wet it under the tap. That did not take too long, but then Leah had to mix it with the handle of the washing-up brush. That seemed to take forever.

Leah sat down with my bucket of feed, right in front of my stable, but too far away for me to reach. All I could do was watch as she mixed ... and mixed ... and mixed. I got hungrier and hungrier.

As Leah mixed, she seemed to have trouble controlling the brush and some of the food got flicked out of the bucket onto the floor. I could not believe my eyes, my feed was being wasted! I tried whirling round in my stable, but Leah did not even notice; she was concentrating so hard on mixing. Just when I thought that the whole night would pass and Leah would still be mixing in the morning, when all my feed would have been flicked onto the floor, Liz would come back from talking to someone outside another stable and say to Leah:

"Cayman can have his tea now that it's nice and mixed, thank you Leah."

But then both Liz and I would have to wait for Leah to give it just one more, final mix. It was alright for Liz to be patient, it was not *her* belly that was rumbling.

Greed

There was another time when I got very anxious about food. Liz had already mixed my feed and left it on top of one of the feed bins opposite my stable; as usual it was in my big flat bucket. As Liz brought me in from the field, I could smell my feed as we approached my stable. Although I had been grazing all day and my belly was full of grass, the sweet herby smell of 'Mix' and 'Alfa' was very appetizing. My nose told me exactly where my feed was. I knew that Liz would want me to go into my stable on the right, before she gave me my feed, but I could not stop myself pulling to the left and shoving my muzzle into the bucket of tempting food. I knew that this was very bad mannered.

"Cayman what are you doing?" Liz said crossly, as I tried to gobble-up as much food as I could, as quickly as I could. She pulled hard on my lead rope, trying to get my head out of the bucket, but this had no effect at all. Then Liz did something that I had not expected; she managed to lift the flat feed bucket, with my muzzle still in it. Holding the bucket with both hands, she turned round and was going into my stable. I was so surprised that I lifted my head up from the bucket.

I do not know why, but I thought that Liz was taking my food off me for good, so I barged after her, thinking only of how good the food tasted and how much I wanted to get my muzzle back into my feed bucket. I caught up with the bucket and Liz in the doorway of my stable ... *right in the doorway*. What I had done was barge in alongside Liz, so that we were both wedged, side-by-side and neither of us could move. Liz was still holding the feed bucket with both hands.

As I wanted to get into my stable and carry on with my feed, I shoved my body forwards and we were no longer wedged, but as I did so, Liz made a sharp, high-pitched noise and dropped the feed bucket quickly down onto the floor. Good, I could get my muzzle into it again. Then I heard Liz making another noise that I had never heard her make before, it was as if she was trying to eat air. She was breathing very strangely and her eyes had water coming out of them; she had one hand on her left shoulder. Liz seemed to have gone so weak, that she could hardly put the rails and the wooden board across the doorway. As she left she said:

"It's alright Cayman, it's not your fault." Liz's voice was not like it usually was, it also sounded weak – and she had forgotten to give me my usual night time kiss on my neck, she never forgot that. I knew that something was very wrong ... and I had a feeling that it might have something to do with me.

The next morning Mrs B. put me out. She often did that, so I was not surprised. I was surprised though, when I saw Mrs B. at the gateway in the evening. I wondered why Liz had not come to put me in. When I got into the stable yard I saw Liz, she was waiting for me, but she could not lead me into the stable because her left arm was held up against her chest by some cloth. As Mrs B. led me into my stable, she said to me:

"Cayman you were a *bad* boy to break Liz's collar bone last night, even if you did think that she was stealing your food."

Liz appeared outside my stable, but she did not come in. Some of the other people were talking to her about her shoulder. As I ate my feed I felt very bad for being so greedy the night before and sorry that I had hurt Liz. When Liz came to talk to me, over my door, she told me that she would not be able to ride me for six weeks, until her collar bone was mended. I realized that my very bad manners meant that we could not enjoy ourselves as usual. It was early summer, one of our favourite times for riding and we would miss it. I was cross with myself, I should have taken more care of Liz than I had done. I was *very* sorry.

Mrs B.

When Mrs B. looked after me I knew that I had to be on my very best behaviour. Although Mrs B. is little, she is quite stern. Mrs B. always led me with her hand inside the back of the nose band of my head collar, so that she could let me know if I was going too fast, by making the nose band press against my nose. If ever she thought that this was not enough, Mrs B. stuck her elbow into the bottom of my neck where it joins my chest, to slow me down. Mrs B. only needed to do this in winter, when I was very keen to come in for my evening feed. Usually I walked so slowly with Mrs B. that she gave me the name 'Diplodocus'. She said that that was a big prehistoric animal that walked slowly, like me. I was very careful; I would not want to hurt Mrs B. because she was so kind to me. Also Mrs B. is Corris's person, so if I ever hurt her, even by mistake, I knew that Corris would be so cross that he would hurt me – but *much* worse.

Mr B.

When Liz went to work so far away that she could never put me out during the week, Mr B. who is Liz's father, came to help Mrs B. with me and Corris. Mr B. was my big friend, we liked each other very much.

Mr B. is bigger than most people, but not as big as Ian the farrier. Mr B. handled me kindly and firmly and I felt safe with him. He gave me some things to eat which were little and hard and had a very strong taste, he ate them too, he said they were 'mints'. No one else, not even Liz, gave me mints; just Mr B.

I usually got a mint when Mr B. turned me out into the field. After he had taken off my head collar, I would wait whilst he got the mints out of his pocket, and put one on the palm of his hand for me to take. Although I was always eager to walk across the field to find a good place to start grazing, if Mr B. had not given me a mint, I would remind him that I wanted one by staying by him after he had taken off my head collar.

I liked mints so much, that sometimes I would start to

walk across the field, but then change my mind and come back to Mr B. for a second mint.

Mr B. had a poorly hip, which hurt him, I knew about this, so I was very careful to walk as slowly as I could when he led me to and from my field. I was never naughty. Then, Liz told me that Mr B. had gone to have an operation to have a new hip.

After a long time, Mr B. came back. He was very glad to see me again and gave me a lot of mints; they made my mouth feel hot. As Mr B. recovered from his operation, he started to look after me again, but this time, he could lead me just as fast as Liz did. Liz said that now that Mr B.'s hip was better, he could ride me in the indoor school, but that as it had been more than twenty years since he had last ridden a horse, I must take very good care of him.

I was glad that Mr B. was going to ride me and as soon as he was on my back I could feel that he knew how to ride. We walked round the school, then did some circles, half-halt and halt, Liz said that we looked very good together and that really, Mr B. was more the right size for me than she was. I did not even need to think about being on my best behaviour, with Mr B. on my back I felt safe and very happy that he was enjoying being there; my best behaviour just happened.

Alex

Alex is Liz's niece, she is ten years old. Alex's sister is Hattie who is six. Hattie is very noisy. When Alex and Hattie stay with Mrs B. and Mr B. they come to the stables to help with me and Corris. Alex and Hattie's father is Dave who is Liz's brother. I have only seen him once. Mrs B. says that Dave rides big motorbikes in races – but that he 'doesn't trust horses'.

Liz gave Alex a few riding lessons on Corris, but although Alex tried very hard, most of the time Corris did exactly what he wanted to do. Liz said that it would be much easier for Alex to ride me. I heard Liz and Mrs B. talking outside my stable. Mrs B. said that as Alex went on the back of Dave's motorbike when he rode it on the road, as far as she could see, that was more dangerous than Alex riding me in the indoor school. Liz agreed with her and said that she knew that I could be trusted to take care of Alex. They said that we would all have to keep it a secret; if Dave found out, he might be very angry with Mrs B. and Liz.

When Alex did ride me I had a big surprise, she *really* rode me, rather than just sitting on me. Although her legs did not come very far down my sides and I could hardly feel her weight at all, I certainly could not ignore her rein contact. Liz could see that I was surprised that someone so small could make me work. I had both ears pointed backwards towards Alex because I was concentrating so hard on what she was asking me to do. Liz laughed at me as she said to Alex:

"Well done! you're making him think." Alex made me do: walk, trot, transitions, half-halt, halt and circles, without a rest.

Before Alex got off my back, Liz told her that as I was so

big, she needed to slither down my side a bit, land with her knees bent and jump backwards with both feet together, like doing a parachute jump; that is how Liz does it. The first time that Alex tried this, she landed, then fell over, so that she was lying flat on her back. Liz very quickly scooped her up; it is never a good idea to lie flat on your back by a horse's legs. Liz put Alex onto my back again and this time, when Alex dismounted, she did a perfect slither down my side, landed with her knees bent and jumped backwards like a confused rabbit. Whilst all this was going on, I did not move a muscle – or a foot. Liz told Alex that she was very impressed by her riding and dismounting. She said that she was really proud of me because I had given Alex a lovely ride, put in some effort, and stood very still at the end.

Everyone agreed that it would all be a secret, but I heard Mrs B. tell Liz afterwards, that Alex was so proud of riding me, that as soon as she got home, she had to tell her mother Jane-Ann, but she did so in such a loud voice that her father Dave heard her. Mrs B. said that Dave was not cross with her or Liz; he knew that horses were 'in their blood' – and probably in Alex's too.

Helen's Wedding

By the time that I was only four, Liz was already so sure of my good manners that she took me to a wedding. We had been for a ride with Corris and Mrs B., on the way back, as we went up Church Road, there were a lot of cars parked on either side of the road and people walking up the hill to the church.

"We've timed it just right, the bride will be arriving in about ten minutes," Liz told Mrs B. There were people waiting outside the church gates, they looked unusual because most of the ladies had bright clothes on and some wore hats, but they were not like the riding hats that Liz and Mrs B. wore.

"It'll be good experience for them to stand and watch what's going on." Liz said.

Liz and Mrs B. 'parked' us with our back ends to the wall, so that we could look at all the people. It was interesting watching them, they looked like a flock of twittering birds. Corris and I were so well behaved that some people did not even notice us; others asked whether they could stroke us. I liked being stroked, but Corris did not. Liz warned people who wanted to stroke us that we might snort without warning, and mess-up their best clothes, so not many people did stroke us and Corris was glad.

Some girls arrived, although it was very cold, they did not have coats on. I pricked up my ears because each girl was carrying a bunch of very tasty looking flowers. Some people had just one flower stuck to their chest. When the bride came, she was carrying even more flowers, they looked *delicious*.

Liz said that we could go home as we had now seen a wedding. She stroked my neck and told me how proud she was that I stood still and had such good manners. I did not go to my first show with Liz until I was nine. Before that, when anyone asked her whether I had been to a show, Liz would answer:

"No, but he's been to a wedding!"

Being Clipped

The first time Sam clipped me, I was frightened. She held a thing like a big mouse with a very long tail against my body. It made that part of me tingle and my hair fell off onto the floor, it was strange. I was tied to both sides of the wash box, so that I had to stand in the middle. I knew that with Sam I must behave. She had already sorted me out once, when I tried to play rearing games with people when I was three. Liz was not there, so I had to try to be brave, all by myself.

I was still wondering what I should do, when Sam made the mouse go quiet, put it down and got a warm damp cloth. She wiped me down where the mouse had bitten my hair off, then I was back in my stable having my rug put on. I was glad, because the parts of me which no longer had hair on felt chilly.

Afterwards, when Liz came, I heard Sam tell her:

"He was good, he just stood there looking out of the side of his eye." Liz undid my rug, and I could tell that she was impressed by my new clip. She praised me for being so good and told me that she had been worried that I might have panicked, as I had never been clipped before, but then she said:

"Sorry Cayman, I forgot, you don't do panicking do you!" Liz was right, I could not be bothered to panic.

The Dentist

When Geraint the dentist came, Liz was there. She stayed outside my stable as Geraint put a big metal thing into my mouth, which stopped me closing it. It felt strange, but Geraint was gentle, he let me stand wherever I wanted to in my stable, that helped. If he had tried to stop me moving to where I felt comfortable, I might have been scared.

Geraint rasped my back teeth with such a big rasp that it made my whole jaw rock. I still could not close my mouth, which made my face ache, it was not very nice. I could see Liz watching over the top rail, she tried to reassure me; I could tell from her voice that she was concerned, but I decided that it must be alright because Liz was not trying to stop Geraint.

Geraint finished rasping and released the big metal thing from my mouth, it was a relief to be able to close my mouth and move my tongue again. Liz rubbed my forehead and stroked my neck, she was smiling and looked as relieved as I felt. I thought that this was funny as it was not *her* teeth that Geraint had rasped, but she always worried when I had to have anything done which she thought would frighten me.

Liz thanked Geraint for being kind to me and told him:

"He was looking out of the side of his eye; he seemed to be thinking 'I'm not sure whether I am frightened or not.'" She was right – it was like being clipped – I had not made-up my mind whether I was frightened or not, before it was all over.

Sitting Down

On hot, sunny afternoons when I was sitting down in the field, my manners were not very good. When I saw Liz coming across the field, I felt lazy and sleepy and made no attempt to get up to greet her. Instead I put my head up, so that Liz knew that I had seen her, but then I would usually flop over and lie flat until she was nearly right by me, when I would sit up again.

Liz always approached me slowly and gently, sometimes she would encourage me to stay sitting down, by crouching down herself as she approached. She said that she liked to see me sitting down because I looked sweet. Sometimes Liz sat down in the field with me. She was always careful of where my feet were in case something startled me and I got up in a hurry. Usually she sat with her back leaning against the opposite shoulder to the side where my legs were. When it was time for me to get up, Liz encouraged me by unfolding both of my front legs and stretching them out in front of me. When she did this, I could not pretend that I did not know what she meant.

Liz liked to sit in the corner of my stable. She always sat in the corner next to the rails, so that if I forgot that she was there and did something unexpected, she could get out quickly. Whilst I was eating my feed, Liz would sit and watch me. If I needed help to drink the liquid in the bottom of my flat feed bucket, she would stand up and hold the bucket under my muzzle, tilting it so that I could drink, then she scraped-up the last bits of food which I ate off her hand.

After Liz had washed my feed bucket, she usually left for the night, but sometimes she came back into my stable and sat in the corner again whilst I ate my haylage. When she did this, I would swing my head round to look at her, but not for long, because I had to concentrate on my haylage. Liz knew what I was thinking because she would say:

"No Cayman, I'm not going yet, I'm going to sit here and watch you, but you must be careful not to tread on me." I did not mind Liz staying – it was reassuring having her sitting there, quietly, with me.

The most reassuring thing that Liz did was in the summer when I was twelve. It was in the morning after a ride, so I was not distracted by eating haylage. Liz said that she had not taken the time to give me a big hug for a very long time. She put both arms up, one each side of my neck, pressed her head against the side of my neck, and stayed there. Being hugged felt so reassuring that I put my neck round Liz's shoulders, and pressed my jaw against her back.

After a long time, we heard footsteps, someone was approaching. Liz pulled away from me. For once, it was Liz who looked confused. She seemed as if she could not believe that whilst she was hugging me, I was hugging her too.

I was 'born with good manners'

Chapter Ten

MONSTERS

*T*he world is full of monsters.

Some animals eat other animals, and some animals get eaten. When we were wild, horses ate grass – and got eaten. That's why we always have to be alert, and why we run away first and ask questions later.

Monsters frighten us. When we don't understand what something is, it's best to assume that it *is* a monster and run away, so that if it really is one, we're safe – and if it isn't, we're still safe. People think that we overreact.

Motorway Monsters

When I was very young, the monsters under the motorway bridge used to frighten me.

They were always there. They made different noises: quiet rumbling, loud rumbling, hissing, even flapping. Sometimes they had shiny eyes. They never jumped up from the motorway to get me (although once, when I ran away with Liz, I *thought* that they had), but going over the bridge when I was young was still frightening, because I knew that they were there.

When I was Very Brave

In the summer, when I was six, I did one of the bravest things in my life. Liz and I were going towards Black Ladies Priory, with Corris and Mrs B.. At the beginning of the track where we canter, both of the gates to the field were open; that was so unusual that it made me stop. What I saw next was even more unusual ... it was the most enormous, terrifying monster you could *ever* imagine – bigger than a stable. It was coming across the field, straight for me. Its mouth was very wide, and its long sharp teeth flashed menacingly in the sun as they devoured everything in its path.

The monster made loud clanking noises and its great weight churned up clouds of dust all round its body. I wanted to run away, but my legs were frozen. The monster clanked its way closer and closer, still eating everything in front of it. I knew that it was going to eat me next, but there was nothing I could do. My feet felt as if they had taken root, there was no hope of moving them.

Just as the monster came face to face with me, in a cloud of dust, it must have lost its nerve, or decided that it did not eat horses after all, because it turned and went clanking off up the side of the field, away from me.

I could hardly believe it, I had won! The monster had retreated.

"Oh, well done Cayman!" Liz stroked my neck a lot, on both sides, "You've never seen a combine harvester before have you? You were *very* brave."

The Lorry

The lorry was always in the yard, that frightened me too – particularly if the ramp was down. I had to go round the lorry on my way from my stable to the field, and from my field to the stable. I remembered the long journeys to and from hospital. I was worried that the lorry might scoop me up and take me away; it always made me breathe heavily.

When I was led out to the field, it was not too bad because whoever was leading me was on my left side, between me and the lorry. But when they brought me back to my stable, we were both facing the opposite direction, so I was closest to the lorry. I sorted this out by either tripping on purpose, or missing a stride as we walked together – so that I was one stride behind the person leading me and could get round them, onto their safe side. Even with a person in between, I still kept an eye on the lorry – I did not trust it.

White Stones

When we did 'The Twisters' ride, we went down a narrow lane, past a cottage with a building at the roadside. The building has a corrugated iron roof. When the collie dogs who live at the cottage heard me coming, they turned into guard dogs and jumped onto the roof so that they were about level with my eyes. Their chains clattered on the roof as they jumped about, barking their heads off; it was deafening.

It made Liz laugh when, with two domesticated wolves threatening to eat me – close to my head on my right – I saw a white stone in the grass on my left, and of course shied to the right – *towards* the dogs.

White stones are terrifying; all horses know that.

Donkeys and Shetland Ponies

Donkeys! What happened to their neighs? What happened to their ears? ... and *miniature* Shetland ponies – almost too confusing to think about! What happened to them?

Could it happen to me? I don't understand. Best to avoid them all.

Trains

Every time we went down the lane that goes past John's farm,

Liz would say that I had not had enough experience of trains. Sometimes she would say that a train had just gone, because she could hear it going away. I was not really bothered.

One day Liz said excitedly, "I can hear a train coming!" We stood safely on the grass verge at the end of the bridge from where I could see down the train track below. The clattering, rumbling noise got louder and louder *and louder;* it hurt my ears. A monster, like a snake, suddenly shot out from underneath the bridge. I had never seen anything dart away so quickly. But then I realised that it was still there! It was in front of me and behind me all at the same time. The part of it behind me made me want to run forwards; the part in front of me made me want to run backwards. I panicked, but I could not go anywhere. The monster was so long that it seemed to be darting away forever. I thought that it had made time stop. I was helpless. Then I noticed that Liz was stroking my neck; she was telling me that it was:

"Alright!" she must have gone completely mad.

The Most Frightening Monster I Ever Saw

Now I'm going to tell you about the most frightening monster I ever saw. So frightening that even thinking about telling you about it makes me feel frightened.

Corris and I had just had a good fast gallop up 'Sleeping Beauty's Wood'. The latch on the gate onto the lane was so stiff that Mrs B. could not undo it from Corris's back, so Liz got off me to undo it. Liz almost never got off me for gates, but that one was impossible. Just as Corris and Mrs B. got through the gateway and Liz was about to get back onto me, the monster descended upon us.

Instantly, Corris bolted to the left, to get ahead of it – and vanished. Before I knew it, Liz had clambered up the gate and onto my back. I could feel her sitting very firmly in the saddle; I knew that this meant that we were in danger. There seemed to be a gap in the monster, so we ventured out onto the lane, but there I saw the true horror of the creature. I put my head right up, so that I could see into the distance. It went on for as far as I could see, in horrible mud-coloured, lumpy pieces, each with an enormous multi-coloured tail sticking up in the air. It filled the lane. Worst of all, it was making a strange, loud, repetitive sound. I stood on the grass at the side of the lane. My eyes were as wide as they would go, every muscle was tense, ready to escape in any direction, instantly. I was terrified.

As one piece of monster was about to pass us, Liz urged me on. I could not face it. Corris was so clever and he had already deserted; the situation must be as bad as I thought it was. I ran backwards. Liz let me settle and tried to comfort me by talking soothingly to me. Out of the corner of my right eye, I could just see her wave her arm slowly up and down. The monster piece miraculously seemed to shrink, lower its tail and go quiet. We went past it in 'stop-go trot', which is what I did when I was really, really unsure: I would stop suddenly and go suddenly. I could see that the monster pieces ahead had also shrunk and the ones closest to us had lowered their tails and gone quiet. I did not know why Liz was not scared; I thought that she must have been very brave, or very stupid, as there was still imminent danger from endless monster pieces coming towards us.

Corris returned, with Mrs B. on his back, led by a lady – he was very agitated.

Corris and I did 'stop-go trot' past a few more monster pieces, but then we came to one with its tail still up. Its tail had a picture of another monster on it! We were both alarmed.

Liz laughed:

"Cayman, that's the Welsh flag! As you're from Anglesey and Corris is from Dolgellau, you should both pull yourselves together and go past!"... so we did.

Corris then got in front of me and bolted past the on-coming danger, at a gallop, leaving me to cope alone again. We finally made it to the home side of the junction with The Avenue, opposite Chillington Hall. As the monster was not now coming directly towards me, Liz turned me and asked me to halt. All down The Avenue, as far as I could see, were monster pieces.

"Alright Cayman, now that you're safe, you can stand here and look at them, so that you'll learn something." I did not know what it was that I was supposed to learn. I did not feel safe, and I did not want to look. Liz could tell that I was not happy, so we did not stay long, but she did praise me for being a lot braver than Corris.

When we got home, Corris told me that he bolted because he was a lot cleverer than me, and just because Liz had told me that the monster pieces were simply groups of people from the armed forces, training for 'The Nijmegen March', that was no reason for him not to have bolted for home. Corris was *always* right.

'The world is full of monsters'

Chapter Eleven

GOING TO SCHOOL

*W*hen I was ten, Liz told me that she was going to live in the Cayman Islands. She was very sad that she could not take me with her. Why not? It sounded as though the Cayman Islands were where I belonged.

Arrangements were made for me to go to Rodbaston Agricultural College, on loan. Liz reassured me that she was still my person and promised that she would not leave me there forever.

The big Rodbaston lorry came to collect me. It was driven by Gemma, who was small and very gentle. Ian, my farrier, was at the yard so Liz asked him to load me. Ian was nearly the same size as me and I felt safe when he led me up the ramp, I did not even think about arguing.

After a short steady journey, the lorry stopped. The ramp was put down and I was unloaded onto a completely unfamiliar yard. I put my head up high, to see as much as possible and flared my nostrils. Everything smelled strange. Liz led me down a lane. I could see horses grazing in the distance, in the field on the right. On the left there were gates in the hedge. We went through the fourth gate, into the smallest paddock I had ever seen.

It was nothing like the geldings' field at home at Gunstone, where there was plenty of space for over twenty horses. The geldings' field had a stream where we could drink; we could also stand in the stream under the shady trees to cool down on hot days. There was a bank up towards the farm – we would stand on the top of it when the weather was good, or shelter down the other side when it was not. The best grass was at the bottom of the field, by the Brewood Road. Under the hedge by the lane there were so many different-tasting plants, and near the gate there was a good rolling place – and usually a big puddle where we would also drink. We could spread out all over the field, so that we were with our friends and away from any horses that we did not like. There was space to gallop at full speed. We would wait at the stile by the stream for ramblers coming over the footpath and watch them walk to the stile on the lane, or we could stand by the gate and watch the comings and goings at the houses opposite. Now the geldings' field seemed like a dream.

The worst shock came when I put my muzzle down to graze; there was no grass!

I was used to feeling lush thick grass on my chin. I could eat lazily, the grass seemed to push itself into my mouth. Now I had to make an effort. I had to roll my lips back and snip off a few blades of grass at a time with my front teeth. It was an effort to get enough grass to be worth chewing.

This was serious! Eating grass was what I did for most of every day. I was glad that Liz was still with me in the paddock, she usually sorted everything out, so I was sure that she would take me to a proper field. I was dismayed when Liz laughed at the way that I was having to eat and said:

"It'll do you good – you're too fat anyway." She told me not to worry and went off!

In the evening I was brought into my new stable. It was enormous; high enough for me to have stood on my hind legs and still been nowhere near the roof. It was also long enough to have a back part where I could hide, and a front part where I could watch what was going on. The stable block was a square, all under cover. I could see other horses in the stables opposite and to the right; there were horses in the stables either side of mine – about twelve in all. We had good, thick, comfortable shavings beds, water and feed. The people caring for us were gentle and kind to us all.

The problem was that we were all in a new and strange place, we were not familiar with the noises and smells there, or with each other. We were all very frightened. Because we are herd animals, fear spreads quickly. I was frightened. I missed the familiar smell of my stable at Gunstone and the companionship of my trusted friends there. I sensed that the horses in the stables on either side of me were frightened, I could hear them moving about restlessly, their breathing was anxious. I did not know why they were frightened, but the fact that they were made me even more frightened.

The horses opposite and to my right were all unsettled too, they were moving about in their stables, bobbing their heads over their doors and occasionally neighing for help. It was dreadful. I felt lonely and vulnerable, I did not know any of these other horses. I wondered what would happen to me. I was very scared.

The next morning I was given some haylage and turned out into the paddock again. This time I was turned out with another gelding, which made us both feel a bit more settled.

After a few nights, Liz came back to see me. She greeted me and then came into my stable, she stroked my neck and carefully looked all round me. She always did that, she said that it was to make sure that I was 'in one piece'. I was pleased to see Liz and hoped that she had come to take me home. I was surprised when she just kissed me on the side of my nose as usual and told me that I was being 'very good', and that she would come back to see me again soon.

When the students arrived it all changed! Suddenly, there were so many new people handling me. I had so much attention and so much to do. There was noise and chatter and excitement everywhere. I was washed with warm water and 'apple shampoo'; my mane and tail were pulled, I felt lighter. When a bee stung me above my eye, in the night, I rubbed the hair off because it hurt. The next morning some soothing cream was put on.

All of my tack had come with me, I was glad of its familiar feel. I had a new person called Lee. Lee was big and gentle. My worries went away and I felt safe, Lee would look after me.

Lessons were in the indoor school, which was light, and airy, it felt almost as big as being outside. Because Liz and I did lots of long hacks, I was already fit, so the work was not tiring. Different students rode me – they were all kind, and I tried hard to do what was asked. After lessons I was always rewarded with a lot of fuss.

I was enjoying myself so much that when Liz came to see me, I had almost forgotten about wanting her to take me back home. Liz was very impressed by my appearance, as she gazed at me in my stable, she said:

"Cayman, I had no idea that you are really 'bluey-white' – I always thought that you were 'yellowy-white' – you look so beautiful." I could tell that Liz was pleased that I had settled. I was the students' favourite horse, and Liz was very popular because she was my person.

School got better and better. When the teachers and students saw how I tried my hardest to do everything asked of me, they let me do more and more interesting things.

At the autumn horse trials I was a messenger's horse.

My mane was plaited especially. My rider's job was to collect score sheets from fence judges and to take them to the controller. It was exciting hearing the horses in the competition galloping up the course. I wanted to gallop with them, but I quickly learned what my job was and settled down to do it.

Liz did not go to the Cayman Islands. She said that 'Hurricane Ivan' had done too much damage there, so she would be staying at home. But, as being at school was so good for me, she would be leaving me at Rodbaston until the summer holidays. I did not mind this at all. It was good that whilst I was at Rodbaston, Liz was still able to ride me at weekends. We went on long hacks, just like when I was at home at Gunstone. We went with Gill and Lucy. Gill is a riding teacher, she is so sensitive and kind to horses – she knew what I was feeling. Lucy is a mare. I do not usually bother with mares – they are silly – but Lucy made me feel brave because often, when we were out hacking, she was very unsure and relied on me to lead the way.

When Liz took me to Shoal Common, we could gallop fast on the soft paths in the woods. I felt free. There were sandy banks and jumps. We would canter up a steep bank and balance right on the very top for a moment, before cantering down the other side and jumping the fallen tree. It was exciting.

Once, I decided to take Liz for a ride, which she was not

expecting. We were trotting up a track, when I noticed a path to the left that we had never been down before. The trees were so low and leafy and the ground was so mossy, that even the light was green. The path looked like an inviting magical tunnel. Before Liz knew what was happening, we were cantering very fast down the path. There was a turn, and the first path led to another magical tunnel, which led to another, and another. Liz knew that I had decided to take *her* for a ride; she clamped herself low on my back and let me go. We flew along.

When we came out into proper daylight at the top of the last path, we were right over by the big pine forest, where we could see the old quarry with the lake in it. My unexpected ride made Liz happy.

On Christmas Eve, Liz came to see me when it was very dark. I had been fed and was eating my haylage. She stroked my neck and made sure that I was 'in one piece', and then she sat in the corner of my stable – she said that she just liked being with me. I did not mind.

Not all my work was work; some of it was standing still. I really enjoyed standing still for a whole lesson whilst a light was pointed at my side. I am content amongst people, and the sound of them talking around me makes me sleepy. Liz said that a picture of me – standing asleep – being used as a projection screen for a diagram of horses' anatomy, was in the college prospectus.

I could not believe my eyes when Corris appeared at Rodbaston! When he was put in my paddock we flared our nostrils and snorted at each other, before trying to bite each other's necks and shoulders. Corris always managed to bite me, I was not quick enough to bite him. We did some 'play kicking' (that's where you buck but don't extend your back legs, so that no one gets hurt), before settling down to graze together; it was like being at home at Gunstone. Corris told me that he had been very worried when I vanished. I heard Liz say that he had marched up to her, demanding to know where I was, and that he had done the same with Mrs B.; I was glad that I could tell him that I was safe. Mrs B. was having a knee operation, so he had come to Rodbaston for two terms.

Corris and I were both used in the Stage I exam. That was an honour, some of the other horses were too inexperienced, but the teachers knew that we could be trusted. We sensed that the exam day was important because the students who rode us wore different clothes – and they were nervous. We both tried our best. After the exam, as a reward for being good, Corris and I were taken for a fast hack, just like at home. We really enjoyed the freedom. Lee rode me, and when we got back to the stable yard, he wrote on the big white board:

"CAYMAN IS A STAR"

As summer came, we did more jumping. Jumping always made me feel excited. When I first went to school I was frightened of bright show jumps, I thought that they were going to bite my legs. To start with, taking off was a problem. Sometimes I would take off too far away and 'cat-leap' at the jump; other times, I would leave it too late and then have to jump like a flea. When I got too confused, I stopped instead of jumping at all. But as I practised I got better; eventually I had so much confidence that I was sometimes too excited. Cross country was my favourite though; Liz always asked me to step over things and to jump logs and ditches and streams when we were out, so I wasn't afraid of natural-looking cross country jumps.

Corris had spent eight years in the riding school at Gunstone. He hated flat-work. In lessons at Rodbaston he tried to get out of doing any work by hardly responding to his rider at all – this usually worked. I could never be that naughty. The students dreaded getting Corris for a flat-work lesson. When we started jumping no one could believe the change in Corris: Corris loved jumping. He was brilliant at it. He loved it so much that if a student was cantering a twenty-metre circle and there was a jump anywhere near, even the most competent rider would find them self being taken over the jump. The students fought over Corris for their jumping assessment!

At the end of the summer term, we both went home to Gunstone, for good. Liz and Mrs B. were very pleased to have us back. To show how glad she was to be looking after me again, Liz got me a new numnah, which made my saddle feel very comfortable, then she said:

"Cayman, for a real treat, I'm going to get Sarah to give you some Shiatsu." Liz had a strange idea of what a 'treat' was. I would have been very happy with some carrots or apples, or both; rather than whatever it was that Sarah was going to give me.

Sarah is Harrison's person, she understands horses. Whilst I was in my stable, she felt all over my body by pressing parts of me; no one had ever done that to me before, but I did not mind – Sarah was kind and gentle. Sometimes I felt hot, sometimes cold, and other times I felt tingling. Sarah stretched my legs; when she did my back legs I felt energy flowing in my back – the feeling surprised me – then my back felt loose and free. The best thing was when Sarah pinched around the edges of my ears, that was nice; it made me feel peaceful and sleepy. I did get some carrots too. I was glad that I had been to school, but happy to be home again at Gunstone, with Liz.

'As summer came we did more jumping'

Chapter Twelve

MY RIGHT LEGS ARE TOO SHORT

I could canter circles, both to the right and to the left, with no problem – when I was three. At five, I found it tricky to lead with my left leg. By the time I was ten, I flatly refused to even try to canter left circles. I would stop dead, put my ears back and swish my tail. When Liz insisted, I did *big* bucks.

Liz was concerned, she knew that I was usually so willing and good. She said that as I was not lame and could do everything else, she suspected that I could not canter left because I thought I could not canter left. She said that she wanted to help me and that she would ask a lady called Julie Dicker, who could communicate with horses, to try to find out from me what the problem was. She cut off a small piece of my mane, which she said she would send to Julie Dicker. Liz told me that Julie Dicker would communicate with me *in my thoughts*, and that I should tell her everything that I wanted Liz to know.

Julie Dicker did communicate with me. I was relieved to be able to explain to her that I was happy and that people were very kind to me, but that: my neck was wrong on the left side, from halfway down, to my shoulder; and that my right shoulder was lower than my left shoulder – which tipped me to the right. I said that all of my left side was a bit taller than my right side, which is shorter, especially behind, and that it was difficult for me to strike off to the left, as my right hind leg was too short. I said that it was really annoying, but not painful.

Julie told me that she would pass this information onto Liz, with her ideas for helping me and that she would let Liz know that I was a kind horse who was not being deliberately naughty.

Liz told me that Julie Dicker had telephoned her to tell her what I had said, and that she had arranged for a chiropractor to come to see me at Rodbaston. When the chiropractor arrived she said that I was 'a lovely horse'. As she started to examine me, she told Gemma – who was holding me – that she needed me to:

"Move over." Immediately, I stepped sideways with both my front and hind legs. The chiropractor seemed surprised, but pleased. 'Over' was one of the commands that Liz always used in the stable.

The chiropractor stretched one of my back legs. As she held it she said to Gemma:

"We could do with a bit more stretch." That was another

word I knew. In the stable Liz often picked up one of my front legs and held it firmly round my fetlock, whilst I stretched my neck and back by pulling away from it, and sinking my back down with my neck arched. Liz encouraged me by saying:

"S-T-R-E-E-E-T-C-H." So, although she was holding my back leg, I knew what the chiropractor meant and immediately stretched my leg much further back. The chiropractor seemed amazed and said to Gemma:

"He understands language! Does his owner talk to him?" Gemma replied that Liz talked to me all the time.

The chiropractor found that the bones at the top and halfway down my neck were rotated to the right; even my head was not on straight! My right shoulder was further back than my left shoulder and my pelvis was tilted so that my right hip was lower than my left hip. She said that to me, this would feel as though my right legs were shorter than my left legs. *That's exactly what I told Julie Dicker!*

As I was a grown-up horse of eleven by this time, and my muscles and skeleton had developed to compensate for my lopsidedness, Liz decided that she would not make an issue out of me not being able to canter left. If I felt that I could do it I would, if not, it did not matter for what we did, which was mostly lovely long hacks.

When I was back home at Gunstone, we had a jumping lesson with Will, who was a professional showjumper. The lesson was with my friend Harrison who is even taller than me; he is

17.2hh. It was the best lesson I have ever had. I was very excited and easily cleared one metre. To jump the course I had to canter both to the right, and to the left. Liz thought that it was very funny when Will said:

"He's got *no* problem with his legs! He's nearly always on the correct one, and when he isn't, he puts in a 'flying change.'"

When I was having so much fun, I forgot that my right legs were too short to canter left!

'He's got *no* problem with his legs'

Chapter Thirteen

LOOKING AT THINGS

When I was young people always knew that I was young, even if they did not know anything about horses. Liz said that this was because I had 'confusion' written right across my forehead. To help me to understand things, Liz encouraged me to look at them. As I grew up, I still found a lot of things to look at.

If I saw something interesting, I stood still, put my head up high so that I could see it better, pricked my ears as far forward as they would go – and looked at it. I had to stand perfectly still to look properly. I did not want to move until I had *finished* looking.

Sometimes, I would think that I had nearly finished looking, but then the thing that I was looking at would move, so that it looked different, and I would have to start looking all over again. If Liz thought that I had looked for long enough, she would ask me to move on. I would let her know that I did not want to, by not moving off instantly, but if she insisted, I would go.

Once, when I was ten, we were on a hack with Lucy and her person Gill, who knows a lot about horses, when I decided to stop and look at something. Liz apologised to Gill:

" I encouraged him to look at things when he was young. Perhaps I shouldn't have allowed him to carry on doing it as he got older, but I didn't think that it would have been fair to stop him; anyway I'm glad that he's the sort of horse who notices things, because it makes him more interesting to ride."

Gill said that looking at things was part of my 'personality', and that it showed that I was thinking. After that, I know that Liz was happy for me to look at things.

The Motorway

One of the earliest things that Liz encouraged me to look at was the motorway. Although I had been very frightened by it when I was only three, by the time I was five I was brave at going over the motorway bridge, so Liz thought that it would be good for me to stand on the bridge and look at the cars and lorries going along the motorway. We would go about a third of the way over the bridge and then Liz would turn me, sometimes to the right, sometimes to the left, so that I was looking over the bridge, down onto the motorway below.

It was interesting to watch the cars and lorries chasing

each other in different directions. I thought that it was strange how some always went one way and some always went the other way; they went very fast and never stopped for a rest. Although they were often in groups, they did not bump into each other, and the ones going away never went to greet the ones approaching.

I wondered what the ones going away were rushing to – they darted so fast; and what were the ones coming towards me in such a hurry to reach? It must be good, because they also darted very fast. Maybe there was really nice food at each end of the motorway?

When the cars and lorries came towards me and went under my feet, it gave me a funny feeling. Although they were a long way below me, I still felt as if they were going to crash into my legs; it was a relief when they did not. To start with, I wondered what happened to the cars and lorries after they had gone underneath me. I knew that the ones which darted out in front of me carried on going in that direction, but where did the ones which came towards me and went under my feet go?

I could hear the noise of cars and lorries behind me, just the same as in front of me. So, whilst the rest of my body faced forwards, I decided that turning my head, so that I could look at the motorway behind me where the noise was coming from, might help. It did.

I could see cars and lorries behind me, darting out from under the bridge. Now I knew what happened to them after they went under my feet, and I knew where the ones which darted out in front of me came from. When I turned my head to look at the motorway behind me for the first time, Liz was surprised, she said to Mrs B.:

"Look, he's worked out that the cars come out the other side!" I got a lot of praise and stroking on my neck for being so clever.

Now that I understood the motorway, it was even more interesting. Liz knew this, and allowed me to stop and look at the cars and lorries whenever I wanted. Sometimes, I rested my chin on the bridge, and looked for a long time. I did get into trouble once though; we were on our way back from a long hack with Corris and Mrs B. and I stopped to look at the cars and lorries. With my chin resting on the bridge and the rumbling sound of the motorway, I started to feel sleepy, so I shut my eyes and had a snooze. Liz was talking to Mrs B. so she did not notice. I woke up when I felt Liz shift her weight on my back and look down so that she could see the side of my face:

"Cayman! You're supposed to be looking at the motorway, not going to sleep!" Liz made the bit press my mouth and squeezed my sides firmly with her legs. I was in no doubt that I had to wake up.

If I felt lazy at the start of a ride, I would pretend that I really wanted to look at the cars and lorries from one side of the motorway bridge, so Liz allowed me to look at them.

If I still did not feel like carrying on with the ride, I would let Liz know that I also needed to look at the cars and lorries from the other side of the bridge, by trying to walk over to that side. Usually though, that did not work. Liz would say firmly:

"CAYMAN, STOP MESSING ABOUT *AND GET ON!*" I did not argue.

Barges

Liz always encouraged me to look at barges, they never frightened me; they moved very slowly and made a quiet chugging noise – like a tractor. To look at barges, Liz and I stood on the bridge where the road goes over the canal on the way to 'The Hattons', or on the path from 'The Woolley', which goes over the canal at Brewood. The Brewood bridge is so low that the people on the barges looked shocked when they looked up, as they went under it, and saw me standing, almost on top of them.

Barges often have flowers growing on their roofs. I was sure that if I stretched my neck enough, I could eat the flowers; I tried very hard to reach them. When I could not, I nibbled the moss growing on the stones of the bridge, but I am sure that the flowers would have tasted better.

The canal bridge on the way to 'The Hattons' seems much higher than the Brewood bridge; it is where I did something when I was twelve, that made Liz think that I was very clever. We were on a hack and as we got closer to the bridge, Liz said:

"Look there's a barge coming, let's look at it from the

bridge." We were on top of the bridge as the barge started to go underneath. Liz waved to the man on the barge and shouted:

"Good evening!" We waited as the barge slowly vanished under the bridge. I could feel that Liz had made the reins go loose, the bit was not pressing my mouth. Usually, when we had watched a barge go under the bridge, Liz squeezed my sides with her legs to ask me to walk on. This time, Liz did not do anything at all. I was curious about where the barge had gone. I knew which direction it went in, so I turned round, walked across the road to the other side of the bridge and looked over it, down onto the canal on the other side. I was not surprised to see the barge slowly coming out from under the bridge. Liz seemed amazed.

She said that she had not told me what to do on purpose, because she wanted to find out what I would do *by myself*, and that I had proved that horses predict. I knew that that must be a good thing, because Liz praised me a lot and stroked my neck, which I like.

Hot Air Balloons

In the summer, just before I came home from school at Rodbaston, Liz and I went to 'Teddesley Park' in the evening, when it was still hot. We went in the Rodbaston lorry with Lucy and Gill, and Toby and his person Gemma. There were two more horses and their people already there. We had fun riding over fields with jumps in; I jumped all of the jumps. When we got nearly to the end, our people agreed that we would all gallop up the last big field together.

Just as we were about to set off up the field, I noticed something strange floating in the sky in the distance ahead of us. It was round and bright. I put my head up, made my eyes as wide as they would go, and pricked my ears. I had never seen anything like this in the sky before. It was strange. I looked at it as hard as I could, but I could not work out what it was. Liz made the bit press my mouth and squeezed my sides:

"Come on Cayman, it's only a balloon!" The other horses had gone; I could see them ahead, all galloping up the field. I had not finished looking, so I did not move. Liz must have known this, because she did not bother me. I put my head up high again, I did not know what 'a balloon' was. As I stood still, listening hard, I heard a roaring sound coming from the balloon and I thought I saw a thin piece of fire under it, but I was not sure – it was difficult to see because it was so sunny. I could not take my eyes off the balloon.

Liz let me stand looking at the balloon for a long time before she said:

"All right Cayman, I'm sure you've looked at it for long enough, come on!" I was not really concentrating on Liz as I walked slowly forwards, my head still high and my ears pricked in the direction of the balloon. Liz got my attention by making the bit press my mouth and squeezing my sides as she said:

"Oh Cayman! *COME ON*!" When I looked up the field, I could see all of the other horses in the distance; they had finished their gallop. Liz pushed me into a trot, and immediately into a canter. I was happy with this, because I could canter steadily, whilst still looking at the balloon ahead of me. I thought that everything was alright, but Liz was still not happy. She pushed me on hard:

"*COME ON CAYMAN*!" I speeded up a bit, but I did not feel like galloping. When we got to the top of the field, the other people asked Liz what had happened to us. Liz explained:

"Cayman had to look at the hot air balloon." The other horses and their people had not even noticed the balloon. Maybe looking at things was only part of *my* personality.

'The Bradshaws'

On the ride over 'The Bradshaws', there is a field with a boggy part just after the gateway and then a ridge that we canter along, before the next gate. We had just started to canter along the ridge with Corris and Mrs B. behind us, when I noticed something dart round – and up – the trunk of a tree immediately ahead of us. Then it stopped, clinging flat to the tree. I stopped – DEAD.

It is a good job that Liz was good at staying on my back when I did things which she did not expect. I held my head high to look up the tree at the flat furry thing. Liz sounded quite cross: "Cayman, it's a squirrel! It's supposed to do that; it probably lives up that tree!"

When I was twelve, we went through the gate again, into the boggy part of the field. This time, there were cattle in the field. Some were to our right by the hay feeder, some were in front of us, and there were more to our left, on the grass. They did not seem very settled – even the ones who were grazing. The cattle by the feeder were walking about; usually they would be eating hay, or – if it had all gone – they would be searching for bits on the ground, like I did in my stable. Most of the cattle in front of us had their heads up, they were looking at me and Liz. As we walked forwards, some of the cattle by the feeder moved towards us, barging into each other roughly. Those who had been grazing also put their heads up and started to walk slowly towards us. I was just thinking that cows did not usually act like this, and about stopping to look at them, when Liz said:

"Cayman, these are bullocks; *DO NOT* look at them, or they will think that you are challenging them." Her voice sounded worried. As we walked onto the ridge, we had to pass the bullocks in front of us. Liz told me:

"Just keep looking straight ahead Cayman."

We walked along the ridge with some bullocks on our left side, walking a bit slower than me. The rest of the herd were behind us, also following slowly. I felt as if the bullocks were all making sure that we left their field. I thought about stopping to tell them that we always went that way and that it was a bridle path especially for horses, but Liz sounded so frightened when she tried to say:

"Walk on Cayman, don't rush," in a calming voice, that I

decided that I should get her onto the other side of the gate where she would feel safer, as soon as I could.

When the bullocks were sure that all we wanted to do was *leave* their field, they slowed down and stopped. As Liz opened the gate from my back, and we went through it, and then closed it, the whole herd stood looking at us, some stamped their feet, others snorted. I knew that Liz felt relieved to have the gate between us and the bullocks. She stroked my neck a lot and said:

"Phew – well done Cayman! I was scared, I thought that you were going to stop and look at them!"

'I did not want to move until I had *finished* looking'

Chapter Fourteen

MY FAVOURITE RIDES

*T*was not trying to be naughty, but sometimes I had very definite ideas about where I would like to go and made these clear to Liz by trying to go that way, even when I knew that she wanted me to go the other way. Sometimes Liz would let me go part of the way that I wanted to go, so that I could see what was there, then we would turn round and go her way – I did not mind that, but usually we stood and sorted it out. Liz would keep asking me patiently and firmly to go the way she wanted, she did not get cross with me. Sometimes this would take longer than other times. Liz always won; but then the next time we were at the same place, she would say to me:

"We can go your way this time." That was fair.

Once, when I was quite young, I tried to do my shortest ride ever. As usual, Liz got onto my back off the ramp to the trailer outside my stable. When she had tightened the girth and organised her stirrups, she asked me to walk on; past George and Rupert's stables, past the lorry (I was not really frightened of the lorry when Liz was on my back), and out of the gateway. Liz asked me to go down the road which runs along the back of the stables. At the end of the wall with flowers on is a black door. As we approached the door, I saw that it was open. What I saw through the door was familiar; this was where my stable was. I could just go through the door, back into my stable. Liz did not agree with my idea, she told me:

"Cayman, we have to do a ride that takes longer than thirty seconds!"

'The Twisters'

'The Twisters' is a ride which is like a really exciting game. Liz told people who did not know 'The Twisters' that it was 'a horizontal helter-skelter for horses'; a series of right-angle bends in quick succession, on a narrow green lane, between high hedges.

When I was young, I could only do 'The Twisters' at a slow trot. Once I tried cantering, Liz was helping me, but my legs were going faster than I could think and I very nearly crashed through the hedge. My problem with cantering left did not help. As I grew up, Liz let me do 'The Twisters' by cantering on the straight bits and trotting on the bends. Eventually, I got quite good at doing 'The Twisters' at a canter, with Liz's help.

In the summer, when I was twelve, Liz told me that she was going to let me decide for myself which way I should go. I was excited and set off at a very fast canter. Liz was sitting lightly in the saddle and gave me a completely free rein. My balance was perfect as we skimmed through the bends, first right, then after only a couple of strides, left, we were going *very* fast. As I approached the next bend, Liz sat down firmly in the saddle and hauled my left rein. I ignored her and went right. It was a good job I did, because that was the way the bend went!

After that, Liz stopped trying to steer me, and let me sort out the rest of the bends myself. When we got to the end, Liz apologised for interfering. She stroked my neck even more than usual and told me that she was amazed that I was now a *really* grown-up, clever horse.

'Flying Horses'

Part of 'Flying Horses' involves going down a long, very narrow, bridle path. On one side there is a brick wall, which is even higher than me. On the other side, a fence, then there are high fences on both sides. It is difficult to get through. A man told Liz and Mrs B. that Corris and I were the only horses he ever saw using the path. I was not surprised because most horses would feel too frightened, being trapped between the fences by the low branches and giant plants. Corris and I were not frightened because we did so much hacking.

In July, soon after I had been so clever on 'The Twisters', Liz and I went down the path again, we had not been that way for a long time – it looked nearly blocked. The trees and bushes level with my head were enormous and leafy and the plants around my knees and chest had spread so that they all seemed to join up; there were spiky brambles too. I could tell that Liz was unsure. I was not bothered though, I knew that if my eyes would go through, then I could get through. I decided to plough on at a very brisk walk. I could hear Liz laughing as she flattened herself on the saddle when we went under low branches. I sometimes forgot that she was a long way above me! I was probably going faster than Liz could think.

Liz kept encouraging me by telling me how good I was being and occasionally stroking my neck, before she suddenly had to duck again to avoid a leafy branch. Liz laughed all the way along the path as she let me find a way through. When Liz was laughing, I knew that she was alright. I also knew that she was relying on me; I was happy that she trusted me.

'Long Hattons'

When we rode over 'Long Hattons', we went past the peacocks which are in a very large cage, right by the path. Sometimes the peacocks were in their shed. Often there were two peacocks and a lot more peahens, sometimes there were pea-chicks too. The problem was that we never knew where the peacocks were, or how many would be there, until we got to the cage. It was a bit frightening. What was most frightening was when the peacocks were showing off – they would spread their tails and rattle them. This was curious and alarming enough, but when they screeched as well, that was too much for *any* horse.

Corris would have nothing to do with peacocks. He usually avoided the cage, by avoiding the path. He was very naughty and went round the other side of the big round bush by the lake. This meant that he walked on a lawn, where he was not supposed to go. He made up his mind – and there was not much Mrs B. could do to stop him.

I was curious though, and because I was curious, Liz and I could stand in front of the cage, looking at the peacocks. One morning it was so sunny that the peacocks gleamed.

"Look at the colour on their breasts, they're blue and purple, and look at their tails, they're green and gold!" Liz *really did* think that the peacocks were very beautiful. I knew that she was not frightened of them; this made me feel better, but I was still unsure about peacocks.

As we were looking into the cage, I noticed something on the floor near to where I was standing, it looked familiar – it was food – and it looked just the same as my food!

I stretched my neck so that I could smell the food. I wanted to eat some, but the wire mesh stopped my muzzle from getting to it. I decided that if peacocks ate the same food as horses, they could not be such a threat to us. After that, I was very brave with peacocks.

'Long Hattons' was an opportunity for a lot of cantering, I usually went with Corris. We could canter from the gate by the bridge over the canal, up the track, to the field. The path through the field was softer – so we could go faster – but it was uphill which was a bit tiring. A hedge runs the length of the track and the path, separating them from the canal. At certain times of year, we had to watch out for the long poles that came over the hedge. The long poles were held by people who sat on the canal bank. They were silent – which was strange, as people usually made a noise. If the poles came over the hedge, it was too dangerous to canter. We were frightened of the poles because they would suddenly shoot over the hedge towards us. We could not tell what they were going to do next, so we went very wide around them, and kept our eyes *and* ears on them. Liz and Mrs B. called them 'perch poles'.

Sometimes there was a barge on the canal. I was not frightened of barges because I could tell what they were going to do next. If they were moving at all, they always drifted along calmly, in the same direction – or they were still. The people on the barge must have been surprised when Liz shouted: "Hello!" to them as we were cantering, level with them, on the other side of the hedge. From the canal, all that they could have seen over the hedge was Liz zooming along, as if she was flying by magic – they could not see that she was on my back.

Next there was a gate, which was easy to open. Liz often said that we should have jumped the gate because there was good ground on both sides. We did not jump it – although I easily could have – because Liz was a bit scared. She unlatched the gate from my back and pulled it open, then we walked through the gap and once we were on the other side, I turned round and walked forward so that Liz could reach the gate and as she held it, I backed to pull it closed; all Liz had to do was lean down to latch it up. We were very good at gates. Jumping would have been quicker, but doing the gate did give me a rest before the really long canter.

As we went over the second canal bridge and turned into the big field, Corris and I would already be very excited. Liz usually said to Mrs B.:

"We'll go first!" We would set off along the track, up the hedge side, at a very fast canter. Just over half way up the field, there is a dip; just as I got to the bottom of the dip, it always made me want to buck, but Liz did not like me doing that, so she pushed me on hard, and I did not have chance to buck. Corris avoided the dip by going along the steep bank, close to the hedge, still at a fast canter. Corris is very sure-footed, Mrs B. trusts him so much that she always rides him with her reins in one hand. If *I* had gone along the bank, it might have made my legs get tangled up.

To make sure that I was *really* listening to her, Liz would sometimes say to Mrs B.: "You go on, we'll walk," and Corris and Mrs B. would canter off without us. I was a bit disappointed when Liz did this, but she would tell me:

"Cayman, I know that you're a herd animal and it's quite difficult for you, but you're *not* joined onto Corris! It's good for your discipline to sometimes walk where you usually canter." I walked along steadily and did not argue. I knew that Corris and Mrs B. always waited for us anyway.

At the top of the field is a gateway where we had to turn very sharply right, but immediately after that, there is another gateway where we had to turn very sharply left. This was trickier than 'The Twisters'. Corris could always do it, at a canter, without missing a stride, with no help from Mrs B.. By the time I was twelve, I could just about do it, at a canter, with a lot of help from Liz.

We cantered up the next field, along the path by the hedge. If there were things in the hedge which might frighten me, Liz would usually see them as well, and before I had chance to get too frightened. She told me: "Cayman, it's just a log." or "Don't be silly, it's only a bird." Liz encouraged me past by pushing me on. It made me feel better when I knew that Liz was not afraid; I could trust her.

The last bit of cantering was along a thin strip of grass by the pine wood, which smelled nice. I only learned to canter along this when I was quite grown-up. When I was younger, I thought that there was not enough space. I used to fall off the grass and get told off for cantering on the road. Corris could always canter on the grass.

We went home again past the peacocks and the lake, with Corris usually taking 'the safe route', on the lakeside of the big round bush, whilst I was brave enough to stay on the path and walk past the peacocks' cage.

'The Long Mile'

Liz says that 'The Long Mile' is her favourite place on earth. It is not really called 'The Long Mile', that is her name for it. It is really Lower Avenue, which is the old carriage approach to Chillington Hall. It is a straight sandy path which is one mile long; there are woods at either side and a wide grassy bridge about one third of the way down. Best of all – it is a bridle path.

Liz has been riding down 'The Long Mile' since she was thirteen. She used to gallop home at dusk, along its whole length with her face buried in her old pony's mane, for fear of seeing the headless horseman and ghostly carriage which – it was said – haunted 'The Long Mile'. She never did see them, and she did not know anyone who had.

The Long Mile is a very magical place, there are spirits there. On Midsummer's Night the spirits are playful. On that night, we always had a lovely ride down the path, weaving in and out of the woods on either side. Corris and Mrs B., and Harley and his person Claire would come too. Harley is a golden Arabian horse, with a flowing flaxen mane and tail – he might be a spirit-horse.

We always stopped at the bridge and I was allowed to graze, the clover there is lovely. People scratch words on the bridge, which stay there for a long time. Liz scratched my name there when I was four. The names of her horse 'Jah' and her pony 'Shandy' were, just, still there.

We went to 'The Long Mile' often because we both loved galloping from the lodge at the end, all the way up to the bridge. When I was young, I used to get muddled-up and try to gallop into the woods on either side, when I was supposed to be galloping straight up the path. Liz had to be ready to sort me out. As I got more sensible, Liz knew that she could trust me to stay on the path. It did not even bother me if there were dogs in the woods. The dogs would bark and either jump about on their leads, or if they were loose, run towards me as if they were going to chase me, because that was what they were expected to do. I ignored them. I had such fun galloping, I felt so free.

Liz always took me to 'The Long Mile' on her birthday and other special days. Last Christmas Day, Corris and I were happy to be taken there. We decided to have a plan for a really good game. Sometimes, rather than going up the path after the bridge, we would be asked to go up 'Corris's galloping field', on the other side of the wood. Corris always galloped up this field. Sometimes I did, and sometimes, if Liz asked me to, I would walk quietly up the field. Although I was eleven, and Corris was twenty-three, he had *never* been as well-behaved as me.

As soon as we left the path on 'The Long Mile', we began to canter. Usually we walked through the wood to the field because of all the lumpy tree roots which could trip us up, but this time we both took-off, straight through the trees and over the roots.

The moment we reached the field, we both turned and galloped. We were neck and neck at 'turbo gallop' (that's what Liz calls it – it's faster than 'working gallop'). Halfway up the field, I went into 'supersonic gallop'. (I had never done this with Liz on my back before; she had to make up a new name for it). At 'turbo gallop', Liz had been sitting in the saddle with loose reins, but as soon as I was in 'supersonic gallop', I felt her get her weight off my back and crouch down close to my neck, she had firm rein contact. We were ahead of Corris who had stayed in 'turbo gallop'.

The hedge by the wood was a blur; I was concentrating on the top of the field. All I could hear was the heaving of my breathing, matched by the gusting wind rushing past us, and my thundering hooves. For once Liz was quiet, she was concentrating as hard as I was; we were together in our own world. We had to trust each other. I trusted Liz to let me go and to balance herself when I did, and she trusted me not to do anything dangerous.

Towards the top of the field Liz sat down firmly in the saddle and pulled me round in a huge loop, in case I forgot that, at that speed, I must not go through the gap in the hedge and onto the bend in the lane. Liz was the most excited and happy I had ever known a person to be. Mrs B. was the same, her face was shining. Liz said that she had never travelled at that speed on the back of a horse before. As we continued home, Liz and Mrs B. tried to work out what had happened. They decided that we had both bolted, but that as we had done it at the right time, in the right direction, they could not be cross with us. Because they knew us so well, they *did* suspect that we had planned it. Liz stroked my neck and praised me even more than usual, she said that that gallop was the best Christmas present she could ever have asked for. I felt happy, and very glad that I had a person who really enjoyed galloping with me.

'The Bradshaws'

July, when I was twelve, was the hottest July ever. It was so hot that some days were too hot for Liz to ride me. I could spend all day standing in the cool stream, under the trees, with Corris. When we did go for a ride, it was usually a long one.

Time is important for people. Liz said that when she was with me, time stood still. She often seemed cross with herself, because she did not have enough time to spend with me. Then, things changed; Liz was with me every day. My back shoes were so worn out from being ridden that my new farrier, Stuart, put some extra metal in them, to make them last longer. We would often be out for so long that when I was eventually turned out into my field, I thought that I would not be able to get enough grazing done before it was time for me to go back into my stable for the night. But I enjoyed our long rides – there was just Liz and me. When Liz did not have another person to talk to, and I did not have another horse to talk to, we were peaceful in each other's company.

The Bradshaws is quite a long way away, so we did not go there very often, but now that Liz had more time, we could go. There is a really good gallop on the Bradshaws, to start it we turned at the metal tank by the gateway. The track ahead of us looked so inviting. On one side is the hedge, and on the other side a big field. The track is wide and grassy, it is long and goes slowly up hill. It is so long that I could gallop and think how good it was to be galloping – and still gallop even more after that. Most gallops, apart from 'The Long Mile', were not long enough; I would just start thinking how good it was to be galloping, when I would have to slow down because we were coming to the end, or we had to stop to open a gate.

Usually, when we did this gallop on The Bradshaws, the field was ploughed earth, which smelled damp and fertile, but in July the whole field glistened with ripe corn, and the air smelled warm and appetizing. The sky was bursting with sunshine – its energy shone into me and it made me feel even happier. I knew when Liz was thinking about galloping, and she knew when I was thinking about galloping. We usually thought about galloping at the same time. So, when Liz said:

"Come on Boo Boo! – let's gallop!" we both already knew that that was what we were going to do. I was so full of joy in the sunshine with Liz, and there was so much power in my back end, that as I surged into a gallop, I felt that if I did not concentrate on keeping my hooves on the ground, it would not be at all difficult to soar into the sky.

Liz told people that she and Mrs B. had seen "The Devil's Horsemen" at Burwarton show. She was impressed by a lady on a white stallion, who galloped with the reins in one hand and her other arm extended sideways at shoulder height, and curved upwards; that lady shrieked and yelped as she rode. Liz was so impressed that she decided to do the same. She was sitting very light and relaxed in the saddle. I could tell that she had the reins in one hand, and she had no rein contact at all. I think that she had her arm up, and she was *definitely* shrieking and yelping; this did not frighten me – I was used to it. I knew that Liz must be enjoying this gallop! We *flew* up the track.

When we got near to the top, I slowed myself to a canter, then trot, then walk, before I halted, stretched my neck and put my head down to get my breath back. My sides were heaving and my neck and shoulders were wet with sweat. As soon as we stopped Liz collapsed flat on my back, she put both arms round my neck:

"Wow! – well done Boo Boo, that was fantastic!" She sounded out of breath too – but very, very happy. We both knew that we would *never* forget that gallop. As we walked steadily past the pine wood, towards the farmyard, we were peaceful. It was a long way home, but we hardly noticed the journey, just the smell of honeysuckle rising in clouds from the hedges that we passed.

'The Long Mile'

'Let's gallop!'

Chapter Fifteen

EXPLORING

I thought that we were exploring all the time, when I was young, because everywhere was so new to me, but Liz had been riding around Gunstone since she was thirteen – so she already knew lots of rides, and Mrs B. and Corris had ridden along every bridle path within ten miles of Gunstone. Between them, Liz and Mrs B. nearly always knew where to go, so we did not really have to go exploring very often.

One of the times when we did need to explore, was unexpected. Liz and I – and Mrs B. and Corris – were going up the edge of Sleeping Beauty's Wood, on our way home. The bridle path runs along the high wall that separates the wood from Chillington Park. The wall is so high that no one could ever see over it. Mrs B. called the wood 'Sleeping Beauty's Wood' because it is very quiet and still. The wood seemed to be asleep. It is a magical place.

The path is not used much because it is often very boggy in the middle, so the wood is not disturbed. Corris and I were not afraid of bogs. Corris was very good at carefully picking his way through anything. He was so sure-footed that Mrs B. trusted him completely, she gave him his head to decide their path for himself; she said that he was 'like a mountain goat'. As my stride was longer, I was usually in front of Corris, so I could not follow his path.

I have always been very willing. Liz said that riding me was 'like driving a Chieftain Tank,' because wherever she pointed me I would go, through thick and thin. That was true. I used not to think much about where I was putting my feet. If Liz wanted me to go in a particular direction, I went without asking questions. I trusted Liz, but this did mean that she had to do the thinking and she had to be careful that I did not get into any ground that was not safe. There was not much chance of any problem though, because I was so big and so strong, and my legs and the backs of my hooves were protected by such dense hair, that I could trudge through just about any mud, water or brambles. As I got older, I did learn to think about where I was putting my feet and I was quite good at finding my own path through boggy ground (although not as good as Corris) so Liz could trust me.

The day when we had to go exploring was in autumn. We had started to go down the boggy part of the path, but in front of us we could see an enormous fallen tree, it was right across the path. Usually we would be able to find a way, either over or under a fallen tree – but this one was impossible. It was an old tree which must have blown over in the night. The top of the trunk was higher than my back. It had come crashing down so that its upper branches were crammed and crushed against the wall, and its lower branches made an impassable barrier beneath the trunk – the path was completely blocked. We did not want to turn round and go back the way we had come because we were all quite tired and it would have taken ages to get home that way. Liz and Mrs B. decided that there was nothing else for it, we would have to go exploring, to find another way out of 'Sleeping Beauty's Wood' – and get home.

I went first with Liz; we turned off the path and she asked me to go through some thick brambles – there was a low bank – and then we were in the wood. The brambles did not reach my knees, so I did not mind. It was harder for Corris as the brambles were up to his knees, but he still picked his way through.

Once we were in the wood, Liz and Mrs B. decided that we should go in the direction of the lane that we had been trying to get to. The wood was quite dark and there was no path to follow. For once I knew that Liz was unsure about where we were going – that made me unsure too. I was not frightened, but I knew that I had to help Liz to find the way out – I had to think too. Exploring was exciting!

Liz encouraged me on through the wood; apart from the snapping sound as Corris and I walked on twigs, it was quiet. The wood felt very big. I sensed that even Corris was uncertain. We were all relieved when ahead of us it seemed to get lighter. We came to a clearing from where we could see a high old hedge and through a big gap in the hedge, we could see a field.

"Let's see whether we can get into that field, then maybe we can find a way out onto the lane," Liz called to Mrs B..

The problem was that there was a deep, wide stream preventing us leaving the wood. We walked alongside it, looking for a place to jump, but there wasn't one. The stream was too wide and the ground was far too boggy for us to take off. Then, further up the stream, right opposite the big gap in the hedge on the other side, we saw an old wooden bridge. It looked as if it had not been used for a very long time. It had plants growing all over it. As we got closer, we could see that there were holes where planks were missing. It did not look safe.

Mrs B. took Corris to the edge of the bridge; she let him make up his own mind about it and then sat very quietly on his back whilst he carefully picked his way over. The bridge made cracking noises as he did so, and bits of wood fell into the stream.

Liz took me to the edge of the bridge, but I could tell that it would not take my weight. Liz must have thought the same because she did not even try to encourage me over. Instead, Liz got off my back. I was surprised when she ran the stirrup irons up and tucked the leathers into them so that they could not flap about and then unbuckled my reins from my bit, pulled them over my neck and held them in a bundle in her hand.

"Right Cayman, you've got to be very clever and get *yourself* over this stream." She said. Liz stroked my neck – and then walked off! I watched in amazement as she went over the bridge. She was in no danger; with her thin body, she hardly weighed anything. Liz got to the other side and then walked back towards me, along the far side of the stream.

"Come on Cayman, you've got to get yourself over. I know you can do it!"

I could see Corris, by this time in the field smugly eating grass, with Mrs B. sitting on his back, waiting for me and Liz. Liz was obviously expecting me to jump the stream, but it really was enormous, even for me. I hoped that there was another way to the field, that no one had noticed. I trotted along my side of the stream, up to the bridge and back again, just in case I could find another way across, but there wasn't one. I was getting very anxious. Liz, Corris and Mrs B. were all on the other side; it felt wrong that I was not with them. I was a herd animal and they were my herd. I was starting to get frightened.

"Come on Cayman – *jump* – or we'll go without you!" I could not believe what Liz said! How could she even *think* about going without me? She must have meant it though, because she turned her back and walked off towards Corris and Mrs B.

I did not want to be abandoned here in the quiet, still wood; it would be frightening if I was alone. I trotted up and down the bank again. I knew that it was useless, but I could not think what else to do. Then, as I stood back where I had started, I felt the pull towards Liz, and Corris and Mrs B. so strongly that all of my energy seemed to go into my back legs, which *pushed* me – in a huge leap – over the stream. I was amazed to find myself on the other side! As I stood trying to work out what had happened, Liz came rushing towards me, smiling a lot. She gave me an enormous hug:

"Well done Cayman! I *knew* you could do it!" I hardly noticed Liz buckling the reins onto my bit and getting onto my back. When we rejoined Corris and Mrs B., Corris asked me what I had been messing about at, and told me that I had missed eating lots of lovely grass.

We walked up the side of the field. Across the next field, we could see the hedges that ran either side of a farm track which led onto the lane that would take us home. It was easy to see where to go, once we were out of the wood. The gate onto the farm track was not locked and we were soon all back on familiar ground. Exploring had been exciting, but I did not want to do it too often.

Another time when we went exploring was in the summer when I was twelve. Liz and I had gone to The Bradshaws and as it was so hot, we had only cantered up the track alongside the hedge, where we usually galloped. To go home we always turned right, but this time, Liz asked me to turn left. She said that there was another path that way, that she used to ride down and she wanted to see whether she could remember it.

I was interested as we went down the path, because I had never been there before. There was a field over the hedge on my left side and a wood on the right. Liz seemed to know where we were going, so I did not worry. But then, we came to a cross roads.

"If we go left, we'll be going back where we've come from – and if we go right, we'll just come out on the road," Liz said. "We might as well go straight on, but I don't know where it leads."

We were both in a mood to explore, so we went straight on, down a path which ran along the side of a big cornfield. To start with, it was lovely – the path was very wide and its long rough grass made the ground softer under my feet. As the path went further into the field, it got narrower; it was fenced-off from the rest of the field by a wire fence. There were houses in the distance and as the path got closer to the houses, it got even more narrow. We kept on walking. When the path reached the houses, their high wooden garden fences were on the right side; on the other side was a high wire mesh fence with an even higher thick hedge behind it. It felt like a tunnel, now the path was only a bit wider than my body. Liz sounded surprised:

"Oh dear, I think it must be a footpath! Horses are *not really* supposed to go down footpaths, they're for people and dogs; I hope no one comes the other way. We'll carry on to the end and see whether we can get out onto a road. If we can't, you'll have to go backwards, it's too narrow to turn round." At the very end of the path we came to a stile with a pavement on the other side. We could not get out.

"Oops! Sorry Boo Boo – you'll have to reverse."

I was not impressed by Liz's exploring – or by her suggestion of what to do. I did not feel like walking backwards all the way to the field. *Someone* had to take charge of the situation. I pulled my back end in as much as I could, drew my nose right into my chest and started to turn. The wooden garden fence creaked loudly as I was halfway round. It was a good job that it was wood, because it could bend a bit to allow my rump to squash round. I was relieved to be facing the right way again and walked quickly back to where the path got wider. Fortunately we did not meet any people or dogs.

I had heard that when the weather was hot, people could do some very silly things. Liz's idea of exploring must have been one of them. I thought that it would be best if Liz stuck to paths that she really knew in future, and forgot about exploring.

'I *thought* that we were exploring'

Chapter Sixteen

PHOTOGRAPHER'S ASSISTANT

My Tail

*M*y tail was at the back of me; it was useful for swishing away flies in summer. I clamped it down tight if I was nervous, and held it up high when I was playing. Most of the time it was just there, and I did not need to think about it.

I could not understand why Liz wanted to take a photograph of my tail. It was when I was six; she came into the field and greeted me as usual, but then she went behind me. I thought that she wanted me to follow her, she usually wanted me to go in the direction that she was going, so I turned round to face her. Instantly, Liz went behind me again. Wanting to do the right thing, I again turned to face her. Once more Liz was not there, she was behind me. I could not work it out, so – instead of moving my feet – I just looked round at her in confusion; that is when she photographed my tail.

The Motorway Bridge

By the time that I was eleven, I was so brave on the motorway bridge that I helped Liz with her campaign about the height of the motorway bridge fence. She said that it was so low that it was dangerous for riders on big horses, if the horses got frightened of the traffic on the motorway below, and played up.

A lot of horses would not even go onto the bridge at all, others had to be led over. I was happy to stand on the bridge and have my photograph taken – although I did keep one ear on the photographer and one ear on the motorway. I was so brave that Liz could take a photograph of her view of the motorway, from my back, to show how scary it was.

Because of our campaign, mounting blocks were put at each end of the bridge, so that riders could get off and lead frightened horses over, then get back on to them again safely. Liz and I did not need to use the mounting blocks though, because I was not frightened.

Toadstools

In autumn, when we were cantering down a grassy track in the wood at Chillington, there were three huge, bright, spotted toadstools in a row along the path in front of us. I was careful to canter round them. When things look *that* strange it is often a warning to animals that they are very poisonous and must not be eaten; people do not seem to know this. Liz was very excited:

"Cayman look at those beautiful toadstools; I wish I had brought my camera!" She did get excited about some strange things.

Liz did not forget about the three toadstools. Late one afternoon, she got me in. I hoped that she was going to give me my feed early, but she told me:

"We're going back to Chillington to photograph the toadstools; we've got to rush because the light is going. We can't go tomorrow because I am going on holiday and if we wait till I get back, they'll be all shrivelled-up." The thought of 'shrivelled-up' toadstools made me feel very uncomfortable, they would certainly be even more poisonous then.

It did not take us long to get to The Lodge Gates at Codsall Wood, we trotted most of the way. We knew that we had to go left at Rookery Paddock – not through the sheep field – we kept going towards Langley Gate. All the time, Liz was looking for the toadstools. We carried on, past The Decoy and then towards Brick Kiln Gate. The whole route was four miles, we had covered more than half and still not seen the toadstools. In the wood there was less light, it was getting gloomy, Liz was worried:

"We might have missed them! Let's go back the way

we've come." We turned round and cantered back; I was looking too, but there were no toadstools.

"They're probably further on ..." Liz did not sound at all sure. We turned round again. When we reached the place where the path split, Liz asked me to go left; I thought that we should go right, but I did not argue, and cantered up the path. Liz realised her mistake:

"Sorry Boo Boo, we should be going the other way!" She turned me round again, I instantly retraced my steps, at a canter and, *without* Liz's help, took her up the correct path. We cantered along a straight grassy track which looked familiar. At last – in front of us, were the toadstools.

It looked as though other animals had walked over them. They had bits missing, in fact, one whole toadstool was missing. Liz found it in the grass and put it back so that all three toadstools were in a row like they were when we first saw them. Whilst Liz rearranged the toadstools and took photographs, I enjoyed eating the long sweet grass. Horses did not usually graze in the wood, the grass tasted different from the grass in my field, it was fresher and more juicy. Liz knew that she did not have to hold onto me; I would not go far when I had such tasty grass all around me.

Chillington Park

In September, I heard Liz tell Mrs B. that she wanted a picture of me. I was confused, she was *always* taking photographs of me, she must have a lot by now. She said that it was to be taken in Chillington Park, by 'The Sham Bridge', in the mist.

Most nights, when Liz put me into my stable, she told me that she would get up very early the next morning, to see whether it was misty. She said that I must try to stay clean and that she would make sure that my tack stayed clean.

Most mornings, when Liz put me out, she said that she had checked, but it had not been misty. I was surprised when one morning Liz arrived at my stable whilst we were all asleep. She sounded very excited:

"Cayman you must wake up! It's misty! You can have your breakfast when we get back."

As we walked down the back road, towards the farm where Harrison lives, I was still asleep. When we reached Harrison's farm I could not see him in the field; I was sure that he would still be in his stable, asleep. Liz did make me do some strange things. By the time we got to 'The Lodge Gates', I was nearly awake. The woods were more misty than the lane; 'The Sham Bridge' was still a long way away, Liz pushed me on. We could not trot and canter all the time though because she said that I must not get sweaty – that would not look good in the photographs.

When we did arrive at 'The Sham Bridge', Liz jumped off me. She checked all round me and seemed satisfied with my appearance. She positioned me on the bridge, with my reins well up my neck – and walked away. It was very early, I had not had any breakfast and I was really hungry, so I put my head down to graze. *Instantly*, Liz walked back to me, pulled my head up from the grass, repositioned me and told me sternly:

"Stand up!" She walked away again. I did not understand; my head just went down to the grass, I could not stop it, the grass looked so inviting. Once again, Liz marched back and firmly repositioned me. I was confused. If this was a game, it was *not* much fun.

Liz put a small shiny thing into her mouth. If she was eating, why couldn't I?

Then, Liz made a noise that I had never heard a person make before – a piercing squeak. My ears pricked and my eyes widened. She did it again – my back tensed. When she did it the third time, I was not really so scared. Nothing bad had happened after the first two squeaks, and I trusted Liz. I looked at her, trying to work out what had happened; she did not usually squeak. I took a few steps towards her so that I could investigate better. This was probably not what Liz wanted because she let out another, longer squeak. I thought that it was curious that my person had started to squeak; it could be a problem because I had got used to her always talking calmly to me.

When anything was wrong with me, the vet was called; I was just wondering whether Liz needed the vet, when she spat the small shiny thing out of her mouth. This time I noticed that it was on a string round her neck, so it did not fall onto the ground. Liz was striding up to me again when, from the wood on the other side of the bridge, I heard *the most blood curdling screech* I had ever heard in my life. I was not going to stay to find out what terrible horse-eating creature made that noise; I was off – at top speed! As I shot past Liz, she lunged at me, grabbing my rein. I whirled round and stood rigid with fear and confusion, looking into the wood to see whether the awful creature had come after me. Liz had *no idea* of the danger I was in ... she just took yet another photograph of me.

When we arrived back at the yard, Mrs B. thought that it was very funny that I had tried to escape into over five hundred acres of parkland, just because I had heard a pheasant. Liz told me:

"You're more flouncy than a supermodel Cayman!" but she did – at last – give me my breakfast.

'I could not work it out'

Chapter Seventeen

MY HOLIDAYS

Ynyslas

I have been on holiday twice: first when I was eleven, and then again when I was twelve.

When I was eleven, I went to Ynyslas with Lucy and Toby from Rodbaston, and my friend Harrison who lives near to Gunstone. The journey was long, towards the end I could smell a familiar smell that I had not smelled since I was very young, it was fresh and salty. I told Lucy and Toby that we must be coming to a sea, like at Anglesey where I was born. Lucy and Toby did not know what 'a sea' was – I felt knowledgeable.

When we arrived, Harrison was already there with his people, Sarah and Jonah – both on his back together. As Harrison is even bigger than me, he could easily have carried people all along his back. Harrison was very excited, he let us know that he had beaten us all, and that he had seen a place where the whole world was covered with water which was moving. I could tell that Harrison was trying to sound brave, but that he was really a bit scared by the sea.

Toby and I were turned out into a small paddock to stretch our legs and graze. Lucy had her own paddock because she is a mare; they can be a bit silly. The field next to our paddocks was 'a people field'. I had never seen 'a people field' before. The people were not grazing, which was a shame as they had more grass than us, they were just walking about. They had low triangular shelters. The shelters were not much good because the people had to fold up and crawl into them, which looked difficult. I liked having 'a people field' close by, it was interesting to watch and made me feel safe in my new paddock. Our people went off and we all got on with eating grass – like the air, the grass was salty.

Later, we all went up the road to the beach. As we reached a junction and turned right, Liz pointed to the left:

"This is where Corris used to live, his field was just up there, opposite the golf course. In those days his name was Prince William!" I was glad that that was not *my* name.

Because I was naturally brave, I led the way. Liz was proud of me:

"Cayman's like a seasoned old trekking horse who has been leading rides his whole life," she told the others. I was enjoying myself, there were so many new sights and smells.

Sometimes Harrison came up by my side, sometimes Lucy or Toby, but I always led.

We walked down a lane which became a sandy track, and then we were on an enormous flat area of firm sand. There was a lot of water in front of us – on the other side of it were green hills. Lucy and Toby thought that this must be 'the sea'. We were all excited, walking eagerly in a row, with our ears pricked, nostrils flared and eyes wide. We turned and walked onto the softer sand, through some little wooden posts – being careful not to knock our legs – and round the end of some sandy hills with rough spiky grass growing on them. Then we saw:

THE REAL SEA! ...

It was the biggest thing I had ever seen in my whole life. It was *very* powerful, moving and roaring all the time, but I was not frightened to approach the sea; we kept walking right up to the edge of the water. Liz asked me to walk into the water. I had never walked into such a huge amount of water before, or into water which moved like that, but the water round my hooves was low and the movement felt gentle, so I did not mind. Liz was talking to me all the time, reassuring me. She knew that I was a bit hesitant, but not really frightened. We kept on walking until the water was up to my knees, it slowed me down a bit. Lucy was quite brave for a mare, she came into the sea behind me. Toby is an eventer, he was used to doing risky things, he came into the sea at the side of me – and just kept going! As Toby was the smallest of us all, this was not a good idea. When the water was up to the top of his legs, Gemma stopped him.

"He'd carry on until he got to Ireland!" she called out.

Harrison was not so keen on the sea. Despite his earlier boasting about seeing it before us, he had to be coaxed into the water by Sarah, and did not want to go in too deep.

We all trotted together in the sea. It was more difficult than usual to move, which felt strange. We had to lift our knees very high. The water swirled around us, it felt cold to start with, but then soft on our legs. There was water in the air so high that we could feel it on our ears. When we cantered, the sand felt comfortable to our hooves, there was so much space, and the air in our nostrils was fresh. Toby, Lucy and I all cantered in one powerful row.

Harrison was not enjoying himself as much as we were. He had been in the sea for a while, trotting along with the rest of us, but he must have been trotting on a sandy ridge, because all of a sudden he fell off it and was in the sea up to his belly – which gave him a big, cold fright. After that, Harrison preferred to stay up the beach and not go in the sea at all.

"He's feeling sick." Sarah said when we got to the sand groynes. "It's not surprising, he's been looking down, watching the shallow waves coming in and going out. Poor Harry!"

Harrison is fortunate, most horses know that their people try hard to understand them; some people are better than others at this, but Harrison's person Sarah is special, she really knows what is troubling Harrison – and other horses – because *she* feels it too. She explained: "I wasn't even looking down at the waves but I felt sick." Sarah kept Harrison up the beach, out of the sea – that way they both felt better.

We decided to go inland on a hack. Liz was in charge of the route. I could tell that she knew where we were so, although we were in a new place I was not afraid, I could trust her. We left the beach up a long wooden ramp, then went up a very steep hill. I thought that it was the steepest hill I had ever climbed ... until we got to the next one! My haunches ached with the effort of pushing myself up.

"Mid Wales is good for fittening horses effortlessly!" Liz called to the others. It did not *feel* effortless to me.

We found a bridle path high up around Borth bog, from where we could see fields of peaceful sheep and cattle. The grass looked lush and inviting; I was envious. From up there we had a better view of the sea, it really was huge, but as we could not hear it or see the waves, it did not even frighten Harrison. It twinkled, I thought that it looked lovely. I would have liked to have lived there – with the sheep and cattle.

Liz said that we would go through Dol-y-Bont, over the back road past Talybont, to Taliesin; she then remembered a short cut to Ynyslas, through Llangynfelin. Harrison and I teamed up and bowled along the two long straight roads back to Ynyslas – at a trot. At 17hh and 17.2hh, both with good bone, we were well matched. Poor Lucy and Toby found all the road-work hard going. It was dusk when we arrived back at "Ty Gwyn" farm. We were all sponged down, and Lucy and Toby had embrocation put on their spindly legs to make them feel better; my legs did not need it. I was enjoying my holiday.

The next morning we were glad to go back to the beach. This time there were other horses there – it was very exciting. We went in the sea again, although Harrison did not go in far. The sun was shining and the sea looked different, it was brighter and the waves had sharp edges. They looked as though they might hurt us, but they didn't, they just dissolved around our legs. We cantered a long way down the beach, and then had a galloping race back. I felt as if I could gallop for ever, it was so easy. I won the race, but then Lucy and Toby kept going, so they both thought they had won. Harrison came last – he said that he did not know that it *was* a race.

When Liz tried to load me in the lorry to go home, I escaped and trotted off up the lane, back towards the sea. I liked being at Ynyslas so much that I wanted to stay, but I got distracted by some tasty grass – and was caught.

As Corris had not come on holiday with us, Liz said that I must not tell him where I had been, because he would be very cross that he had not been included – especially as Ynyslas was his old home. I was so excited that I forgot, and as soon as I was back in the geldings' field, I told Corris all about my holiday. Corris was so furious that he did not graze with me for a long time afterwards.

Harrison went home and told his companion, Rhapsody, that he had been to another world, covered with water which moved all the time and made him feel sick; Rhapsody did not believe him.

Felindre

My second holiday was when I was twelve. I went to Felindre with Hattie, who is a mare, she is 17hh like me; her person is Lisa. Before we went to Felindre, our people thought that Hattie and I should meet to make sure that we got on. We met at Chillington. Hattie came with her companion, Velvet, who is also a mare. As Hattie and Velvet came up the lane towards me, I could see them both, but I could hardly hear them. When I got up close, I realised why they sounded so quiet – they had not got metal shoes. Their feet sounded hollow like mine used to when I was young. Another strange thing about Hattie and Velvet was that they did not have bits in their mouths, their bridles were different from mine, they were made out of rope. They looked more relaxed than other horses I had seen being ridden.

Hattie and Velvet were content together. They did not make any effort to talk to me at all, so I did not bother to talk to them. As usual, Liz was talking to me, so I did not feel left out and we just got on with enjoying the ride – which was a bit slower than usual because Hattie and Velvet were used to doing shorter rides than me. At the end of the ride Hattie and Velvet put *themselves* into their trailer and went home. I did not think that a whole holiday with Hattie would be much fun, especially after last year's holiday with Harrison, Toby and Lucy.

I knew when we were going to Felindre because Liz got me

out of the field in the afternoon, groomed me and put on my travel rug and a tail bandage; she also put on my travel boots. I did not like those big thick boots, they came up over the sides of my knees – and over my hocks at the back. I felt as though all my leg joints were wrapped up. I could not even walk properly, let alone run away if I needed to. Once, I had tried to shake one off my back leg and had kicked Liz's knee by mistake, that really hurt her.

I could not believe how much haylage Liz had got ready to take for me, it was all stacked up on the feed bins; there were four big nets – and another long bag – stuffed with it. I thought that we must be going for a long time. Liz explained to Mrs B., as they stood outside my stable:

"When we went to Ynyslas, last August, Cayman wasn't having haylage, so I didn't take any, but everyone else had taken haylage for their horses. I felt like 'a negligent mother', because I had packed a dress with sequins for myself, and no food for Cayman! I'm not going to make the same mistake again."

The longest lorry I had ever seen was parked in the middle of the yard. As it was evening feed time, a lot of cars were also parked in the yard and there were people everywhere. Liz tried to load me in my leather head collar, like she did when I was at Rodbaston. I had been very good at loading there because we went in the lorry in the mornings, after I had had some haylage and eaten my breakfast.

This time, I did not want to go anywhere in a lorry. I

wanted to go back into my stable, have my evening feed and settle down with my haylage as usual – so I jumped off the side of the ramp. Liz could not stop me because the lead rope was too short for her to have any control. I squeezed past the cars and, despite my travel boots, trotted round the trailer towards my stable. I was startled as Liz jumped out in front of me, from round the other side of the trailer and grabbed my lead rope.

"Cayman – STOP!" she shouted angrily. As I had stopped by a full net of haylage that had been left for another horse, I thought that I might as well eat that, but no sooner had I opened my mouth to pull a big mouthful of haylage, than Sam was by my head and a severe 'Chifney' bit was slipped over my tongue.

"What are you doing Cayman, carting your Mum like that?" Sam was *very* stern. I knew that I was in trouble. I was wary of Sam after she had 'sorted me out' when I was young and tried to play rearing games with people – but when I was older, I did hear her say:

"He's ever so sweet", so I knew that she liked me really. Liz led me very firmly back to the lorry, which was now parked in the narrow entrance to the yard. I hesitated for a moment at the bottom of the ramp, but decided to go up instantly as I felt tight lunge lines against each side of my haunches ... and heard Sam growl at me.

The journey to Felindre was very long. The first part was easy and straight, but the last part felt as if we were going round in circles; I could feel that we were climbing too. Eventually, I was unloaded and led by Liz up a very steep bank into a paddock. I did not mean to be bad mannered, but I was so excited that I snatched away and went trotting across the paddock to explore. Liz watched me, she was not cross. When I had settled a bit, she took off my rug and boots so that I could roll. I rolled quickly, but just then, I noticed a horse that I recognised in the next paddock – it was Hattie. It was a relief to see her and I felt a bit safer in my new surroundings, even though she was a mare. Hattie had been in her paddock for a while and was quite settled, so I knew that it must be alright here. I decided to get on with eating some grass.

The cottage where our people were staying was right at the bottom of my paddock. In the evening Liz came out with my rug. Although there was a stable for me, she said that as it was May, it would be much better for me to stay out overnight, with my rug on. I was glad, I liked to be outside where I could eat more grass and see what was going on. Hattie was also staying out. Liz emptied one of the haylage nets onto the ground. I had a mouthful, but decided that this new grass was much better than haylage.

The next morning Liz came out early to check that I was alright. As soon as I saw her approaching the gate, I wanted to go to meet her, but the problem was that it was impossible to walk straight down the field – it was so steep that I felt that I would fall over. I had to go down by zigzagging from one side of the field to the other, which was hard work and took ages. That was not the only difficulty though, the ground was so steep that I even felt unsafe walking across it, because one side of me was up and one side was down. I had to concentrate very hard, and my legs already ached from balancing on the field all night; it had been difficult to go to sleep – my field at home was much easier. Liz could not wait for me to zigzag down to her; she came striding up the field straight to me, laughing at the way I was walking. It was alright for her, she only had to cope with two legs. Liz put my head collar on and let me zigzag my way down to the gate. We crossed the yard and went into a big shed, where there was an empty stable for me. Hattie was already in her stable, and we were soon tacked-up and ready to go for a ride.

As we were ridden up the steep path from the gate out of the yard, I remembered the feeling in my haunches from last year's holiday. Hattie said her haunches were hurting her too. I wondered whether holidays always made horses' haunches hurt. We both pushed ourselves up to the first flat place where we could have a rest; from there we could see properly what a lovely place we had come to. We pushed ourselves on, up more twists and turns in the path; as we got higher the ground levelled out. All around us were open fields spread over gentle hills – there were not many trees. It looked like a wonderful place to go for a ride, I was really happy. We walked and trotted on springy grass at the side of a lane. Hattie was enjoying herself as well, and we were friends.

Our first ride was not too long, and after the first bit, not too strenuous. Hattie and I spent the afternoon grazing in the sunshine, whilst our people sat in the garden at the bottom of my paddock. I was enjoying this holiday.

The next morning when Liz came to check me, she told me:

"You know Cayman, if I stand on my bed and look out of the window in the roof, I can see you standing at the top of your paddock! I wish that I could do the same at home – I just like looking at you. One day I hope that we can live somewhere where you are right outside, so that I can always see you." I thought that sounded like a good idea – if Liz could see me more she might give me more carrots.

I was standing on the only flat ground in the paddock, right at the top by the hedge. Instead of standing sideways, like I had to on the rest of the paddock, I could stand with my tail to the hedge, looking down towards the yard and Liz's cottage, provided that I kept all four feet close together, because I was a bit too long for the thin strip of flat ground. This was not how I normally stood, but it was better than having one side up and one side down. Liz was laughing at me again:

"You look as though you're standing on a shelf that's too narrow for you!" she said. Liz got on with taking the manure off the field; I could not help with that job, so I watched. As I watched, I noticed that when she wheeled the heavy wheel barrow down the field, Liz had to zigzag too.

When we went out, we set off in a different direction, down a hard road. That was effortless – but it did not last. Soon we were climbing again, steeply as the lane narrowed. Then, through a farmyard, to a gate on a very steep hill. The gate swung back easily when Liz opened it from my back, but because of the hill, it would have been impossible for her to close it from my back. Fortunately, another horse came from the farmyard, its rider stopped to talk to our people, so Hattie and I could have a rest and we did not have to close the gate. We followed the road up onto flatter ground with hills all around, Hattie and I both felt excited and glad to be there. We had a long canter, side by side, on more springy grass by a stream. We could tell that our people were not really sure where they were taking us, but they did not seem worried. As far as we could see there was grass, streams and hills, so we were not worried either.

We had a surprise when we came up a hill and, on top, found a herd of cattle and calves grazing with a herd of sheep – *and* a herd of ponies and foals. I had never seen so many animals mixed up before; they looked very happy together. I stood looking at them for a long time. Liz asked me to walk on, so I did – but from a different place, they looked different – so I had to stop again. Liz let me stand and look at the animals once more, before asking me to walk on. I walked on, but the same thing happened ... I had to stop and look, because they looked different again. As I concentrated on looking for the third time, Liz interrupted my thoughts:

"Cayman! *Can we get on with the ride?*" She pushed me on so firmly, that I knew that she was *insisting,* not asking, me to walk on – so I did.

We went such a long way that day, past tumbledown cottages, through abandoned farmyards, up the sides of valleys, along ridges, down the sides of valleys. We followed streams, fence lines and sheep tracks. Lisa read the map, Liz and I did the gates. Liz counted that we opened and closed twenty-four gates. We have always done gates; I know what 'B-a-a-ck', and 'P-u-u-u-sh' mean. Liz told Lisa that sometimes she was so far out of the saddle, that she was 'past the point of no return' and that it was only because I was so good and let her scramble about and hang off me, that all those gates got done from the saddle. Liz always let me know that she was pleased with my efforts by stroking my neck and telling me so. I liked being helpful.

Hattie was a good companion, she was steady like me, she did not even panic when we got onto a bog by mistake. Coming down the lanes home was nearly as hard as going up them, we had to brace our legs and backs to stop ourselves slipping. When we arrived at the yard, it was good to have our saddles off and to be turned out to roll. We were both very happy. It was late afternoon and our people went into their cottage for a while. Hattie and I concentrated on grazing, we were hungry as we had not had chance to eat much grass all day. In the evening our people came out to put our rugs on, then went off to get food for themselves.

That night the sheep in the field at the top of my paddock were annoying me with their bleating and coughing, so I went down to the gate at the bottom, where it was quiet.

Hattie was asleep in her paddock on the other side of the fence. I was content and settled.

It was *very* dark apart from the stars.

Much later, when our people returned, I was still by the gate; I had been asleep, but the sound of their car woke me. As I looked down onto the yard below, I saw Liz climbing up the steep bank towards the gate, she was looking up:

"*Wow*! Look at all those stars. It's so clear, it looks as though you could just pick them out of the sky, they're so close. I have never seen such a clear sky!" As she came closer, Liz saw me standing in the darkness, looking over the gate:

"Look at Cayman! He is so beautiful. *He looks as though he's in the stars.*"

The End

Cayman, Harrison, Toby, Lucy

EPILOGUE

*E*veryone who knew me, knew Cayman.

Cayman died in August 2006, whilst I was visiting Cuba; he was only twelve. Mr and Mrs B., my parents, dealt with everything – they were marvellous. Mrs B. broke the news to me immediately I arrived home. In the two weeks that I was away:

Paul, a horse owner from Cameroon, who sat next to me on the flight from London, knew all about Cayman, although this necessitated me speaking French (*not* my usual language), for several hours.

The carriage driver in Havana who took us on a tour of the city in a phaeton, thought that I was going to request the usual tourist memento when I produced my digital camera at the end of our trip, but no – I showed him the photographs of Cayman at dawn, in the mist at Chillington. He spoke very little English, I spoke very little Spanish, but he was enraptured by Cayman, exclaiming:

"El Blanco! Muy Grande!" He had to show the pictures to his colleagues.

Hector took us riding on the beach in Holguin, where he and I had a flat-out galloping race. Hector was seventy, if he was a day, with no front teeth and no English. He rode in a stripped tee-shirt and straw hat; from a distance he looked like a young boy. He knew about Cayman.

Joe from Essex, at our hotel, made the fatal mistake of telling me that he had been an apprentice jockey. An hour-and-a-half, and the digital photographs later, he also knew Cayman.

I hope that *you* now know Cayman ... *he was worth knowing*.

Elizabeth Brown

"El Blanco!"

POSTSCRIPT

The sequence of events which began in September 2006 has been amazing and humbling.

As predicted, I have been led quickly, consistently and deliberately, to an *insistent* colt foal – with a sense of humour. His name is 'Falconwood CaymanHavana.'

... we already know each other.

Elizabeth Brown

If you enjoyed *CaymanStar*,
read Elizabeth Brown's second book,

CaymanHavana
The True Story of a Horse's Return

For nine years, from the age of three, Cayman had grown up to become more than Liz's friend; he was her rock. A beautiful, dappled grey horse, kind and gentle, with a sense of humour.

Now, he was gone. The sledgehammer of shock felled Liz when she arrived home; two idyllic weeks in Cuba eradicated as if they had never happened. As her soul writhed, Liz was sure that she and Cayman had not left each other – and that they never would.

Through a remarkable sequence of events, which unfolded with its own unstoppable momentum, Cayman taught Liz a crystal clear lesson. That lesson was about love – and its *immense* power.

"People need to know about this!
Now, through *CaymanHavana*, you have an opportunity to share a wonderful – and empowering – experience."
Caroline Booth BHSI (Reg'd)
Reiki Master Healer/Teacher, Animal Communicator.

"Awesome, inspiring and compelling. Be prepared…
CaymanHavana will rock
every one of your emotions."
Dr Richard Majors, (USA) Counselling Psychologist and Author.